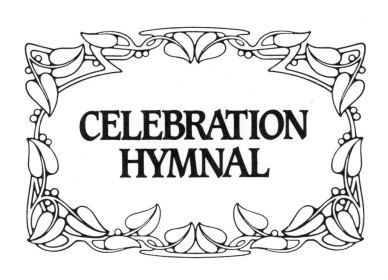

CELEBRATION HYMNAL

Volume 2 (376~722)

Edited by Stephen Dean

McCRIMMONS
Great Wakering

First published in Great Britain 1978 by
MAYHEW-McCRIMMON LTD, Great Wakering, Essex

Reprinted with revisions 1986

Compilation ©1978, 1984, 1986 by McCrimmons

ISBN 0 85597 368 4

Cover design by Jim Bowler
Music Artwork by McCrimmons
Printed by Billing & Sons Limited, Hylton Road, Worcester WR2 5JU

376

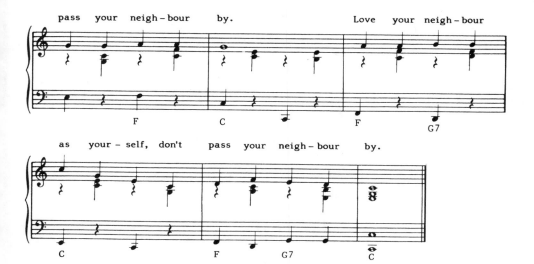

pass your neigh-bour by.   Love your neigh-bour

as your-self, don't pass your neigh-bour by.

2. A certain Levite came that way
   a man of wealth and pride;
   "I'm much too busy to stop" said he,
   and passed on the other side.
   But a certain man from Samaria,
   a stranger in the land,
   took pity on the injured man
   and lent a helping hand.

Words: based on Luke 10:25-37
       by Mary Lu Walker
Music: Mary Lu Walker

© 1975 Missionary Society of St Paul
the Apostle in the State of New York

Harmony: for Celebration Hymnal
         by James O'Donnell

© 1984 Mayhew-McCrimmon Ltd

377

Final Refrain

A child is born for us to-day, al - le ——— lu - ia. He is our Sa-viour and our God, al - le ——— lu — ia, al — le ——— lu - ia, al - le ——— lu - ia.

Fine

Verses

1. Let our hearts resound with joy
   and sing a song of gladness
   for the Lord, our brother,
   is come and we are redeemed.

2. Tell the world of our good news:
   Jesus the Christ is among us,
   and his presence we celebrate
   offering peace and our joy to all.

3. Christ is born, the Christ has come!
   Sing everyone 'Alleluia!'
   Caught in wonder at this birth
   we worship God become man for us.

4. Glory to God, born today
   of the Virgin Mary,
   in a cave at Bethlehem:
   is there room in our lives for him?

5. His name shall be 'Emmanuel':
   'God-who-lives-among-us'.
   Angels sing and shepherds cry:
   'Born is the saviour, our Lord!'

6. The magi went and worshipped him
   with gifts so precious and costly.
   In the fervour of their faith
   they sought the child who is Lord and King.

7. The Lord will make integrity
   and peace grow in our times.
   A covenant he offers us:
   lasting joy will be ours to share.

8. Arise! Shine out, Jerusalem!
   The glory of Yahweh* has come to you.
   Lift up your eyes and look around!
   Radiant is your salvation.

   * *Instead of 'Yahweh' you may
   prefer to substitute 'God'.*

Words and music: Gregory Norbert OSB

378

1. A child is born in Beth- le- hem, al- le- lu- ia:

So leap with joy Je- ru- sa- lem, al- le- lu- ia, al- le- lu- ia.

Refrain

A new song let us sing for Christ is born let us a- dore

and let our glad-ness ring.

2. Through Gabriel the word has come, alleluia:
   The Virgin will conceive a son, alleluia, alleluia.

3. Within a manger now he lies, alleluia:
   Who reigns on high beyond the skies, alleluia, alleluia.

4. The shepherds hear the angel's word, alleluia:
   This child is truly Christ the Lord, alleluia, alleluia.

5. From Saba, from the rising sun, alleluia:
   With incense, gold, and myrrh they come, alleluia, alleluia.

6. Till with their gifts they enter in, alleluia:
   And kings adore the new-born King, alleluia, alleluia.

7. From virgin's womb this child is born, alleluia:
   The Light from Light who brings the dawn, alleluia, alleluia.

8. He comes to free us from our strife, alleluia:
   And share with us the Father's life, alleluia, alleluia.

9. At this the coming of the Word, alleluia:
   O come let us adore the Lord, alleluia, alleluia.

10. To Father, Son, and Spirit praise, alleluia:
    From all his creatures all their days, alleluia, alleluia.

Words: Latin, 14th century, translated by Ralph Wright, O.S.B.
© 1981 ICEL. All rights reserved.
Music: Plainchant, Mode 1, acc. by Theodore Marier.
© 1981 ICEL. All rights reserved.

379

EIN' FESTE BURG 87.87.66.667

1. A mighty stronghold is our God,
   a sure defence and weapon.
   He'll help us out of every need
   whatever now may happen.
   The ancient evil fiend
   has deadly ill in mind;
   great power and craft are his,
   his armour gruesome is
   on earth is not his equal.

2. With our own strength is nothing done
   soon we are lost, dejected;
   but for us fights the rightful Man
   whom God himself elected.
   You ask: Who may this be?
   Christ Jesus it is he,
   the Lord Sabaoth's Son,
   our God, and he alone
   shall hold the field victorious.

3. And though the world were full of fiends
   all lurking to devour us,
   we tremble not nor fear their bands,
   they shall not overpower us.
   The prince of this world's ill
   may scowl upon us still,
   he cannot do us harm,
   to judgment he has come;
   one word can swiftly fell him.

4. The Word they must allow to stand –
   for this they win no merit;
   upon the field, so near at hand,
   he gives to us his Spirit.
   And though they take our life,
   goods, honour, child, and wife,
   though we must let all go,
   they will not profit so:
   to us remains the Kingdom.

Words: Martin Luther (1483–1516)
       translated by Honor Mary Thwaites

© Honor M. Thwaites

Music: Later form of melody by Martin Luther,
       harmonised by J.S. Bach (1685–1750)

380

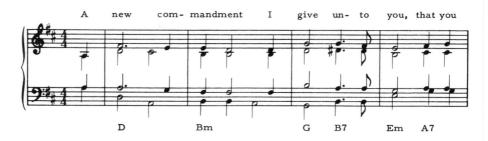

A new com- mandment I give un- to you, that you

D   Bm   G   B7   Em   A7

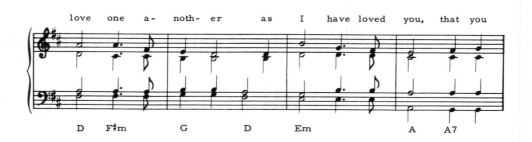

love one a- noth- er as I have loved you, that you

D   F♯m   G   D   Em   A   A7

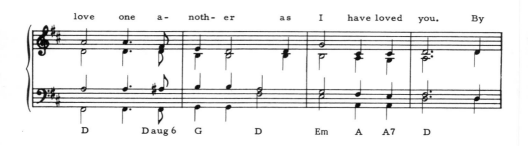

love one a- noth- er as I have loved you. By

D   D aug 6   G   D   Em   A   A7   D

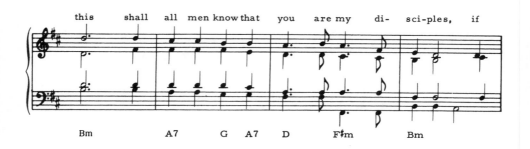

this shall all men know that you are my di- sci- ples, if

Bm   A7   G   A7   D   F♯m   Bm

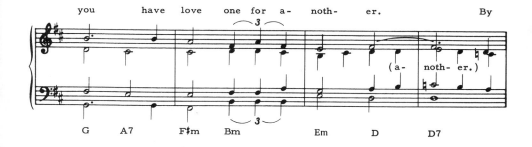

you have love one for a- noth- er. By

(a- noth- er.)

G   A7   F#m   Bm   Em   D   D7

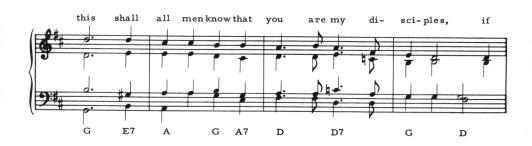

this shall all men know that you are my di- sci- ples, if

G   E7   A   G   A7   D   D7   G   D

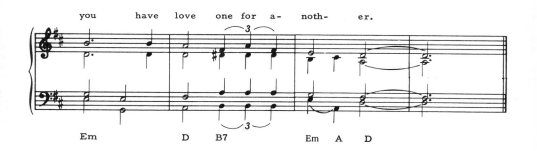

you have love one for a- noth- er.

Em   D   B7   Em   A   D

Words (based on John 13:34-35) and Melody: Source unknown,
arranged by Stephen Dean

Arrangement © 1984 by Stephen Dean

1. A noble flow'r of Juda from tender roots has sprung,
    a rose from stem of Jesse, as prophets long had sung;
    a blossom fair and bright,
    that in the midst of winter will change to dawn our night.

2. The rose of grace and beauty of which Isaiah sings
    is Mary, virgin mother, and Christ the flow'r she brings.
    By God's divine decree
    she bore our loving Saviour who died to set us free.

3. To Mary, dearest mother, with fervent hearts we pray:
    grant that your tender infant will cast our sins away,
    and guide us with his love
    that we shall ever serve him and live with him above.

Words: based on Isaiah 11:1ff.,
15th century 'Es ist ein' Ros' entsprungen',
cento paraphrase by Anthony G Petti
Music: Melody from Alte Catholische Geistliche Kirchengesang (1599)
harmonised by Michael Praetorius (1571-1621)

382

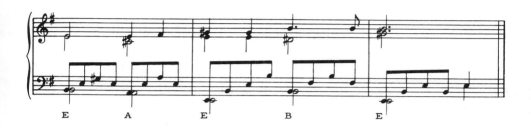

1. A sign is seen in heaven,
   a maiden-mother fair;
   her mantle is the sunlight,
   and stars adorn her hair.
   The maiden's name is Mary;
   in love she brings to birth
   the Lord of all the ages,
   the King of all the earth.

2. Like moonlight on the hilltops
   she shines on all below;
   like sunlight on the mountains
   her Child outshines the snow.
   O Mary, Queen of mothers,
   still smile on young and old;
   bless hearth and home and harvest,
   bless farm and field and fold.

3. Pray, Mother, Queen in glory,
   before the Father's throne;
   praise God's eternal Wisdom,
   the Child who is your own;
   rejoice in God the Spirit,
   whose power let you conceive
   the Child of Eden's promise,
   O new and sinless Eve.

Words: from Revelation 12:1-6,17
       by James Quinn SJ
Music: Patrick G. Fitzpatrick

383

Abba, Abba, Father,
you are the potter,
we are the clay,
the work of your hands.

2. Father,
   may we be one in you
   as he is in you
   and you are in him,
   and you are in him.

3. Glory,
   glory and praise to you,
   glory and praise to you
   for ever. Amen.
   For ever. Amen.

Words and Music: Carey Landry

384

1. Ab- ba, Fa-ther, send your Spi- rit. Glo- ry, Je- sus Christ.

Ab- ba, Fa-ther, send your Spi- rit. Glo- ry, Je- sus Christ.

Chorus

Glo- ry hal- le- lu- jah, glo- ry, Je- sus Christ.

Glo- ry hal- le- lu- jah, glo- ry, Je- sus Christ.

2. I will give you living water...

3. If you seek me you will find me...

4. If you listen you will hear me...

5. Come, my children, I will teach you...

6. I'm your shepherd, I will lead you...

7. Peace I leave you, peace I give you...

8. I'm your life and resurrection...

9. Glory Father, glory Spirit...

Other words from Scripture may be substituted according to the occasion or the season. For example, in Advent:

1. Come, Lord Jesus, Light of nations...

2. Come, Lord Jesus, born of Mary...

3. Come, and show the Father's glory...

Words and Music: Ginny Vissing
©1971 Shalom Community Inc.

1. Across the years there echoes still
   the Baptist's bold assertion:
   the call of God to change of heart,
   repentance and conversion.

2. The word that John more boldly spoke
   in dying than in living
   now Christ takes up as he proclaims
   a Father all-forgiving.

3. The erring Son he welcomes home
   when all is spent and squandered.
   He lovingly pursues the sheep
   that from the flock has wandered.

4. Forgive us, Lord, all we have done
   to you and one another.
   So often we have gone our way,
   forgetful of each other.

5. Forgetful of the cross they bear
   of hunger, want, oppression -
   grant, Lord, that we may make amends
   who humbly make confession.

Words: Denis E. Hurley

© Archdiocese of Durban, South Africa
Music: Irish Traditional

386 CHURCH TRIUMPHANT (88.88)

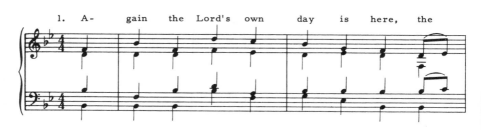

1. A-gain the Lord's own day is here, the

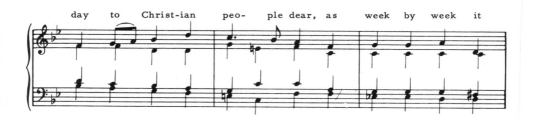

day to Christ-ian peo-ple dear, as week by week it

bids them tell how Je-sus rose from death and hell. .

2. For by his flock the Lord declared
his resurrection should be shared;
and we who trust in him to save
with him are risen from the grave.

3. We, one and all, of him possessed,
are with exceeding treasures blest;
for all he did and all he bore
is shared by us for evermore.

4. Eternal glory, rest on high,
a blessed immortality,
true peace and gladness, and a throne,
are all his gifts and all our own.

5. And therefore unto thee we sing,
O Lord of peace, eternal King;
thy love we praise, thy name adore,
both on this day and evermore.

Words: Attributed to Thomas à Kempis (1380-1471),
translated by J. M. Neale (1818-66) and others
Music: J. W. Elliott (1833-1915)

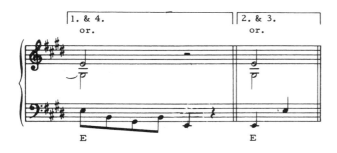

Words and Music: Unknown, arranged by Rosalind Pitcher
© Arrangement Mayhew-McCrimmon Ltd

'Alabare a mi Señor' means 'Praise to my Lord'. This hymn has become a favourite at all large Christian gatherings. The chorus is always sung in Spanish. The final verse may be improvised to suit the occasion.

ALL FOR JESUS (87.87)

1. All for Jesus – all for Jesus,
   this our song shall ever be;
   for we have no hope, nor Saviour,
   if we have not hope in Thee.

2. All for Jesus – Thou wilt give us
   strength to serve Thee, hour by hour;
   none can move us from Thy presence,
   while we trust Thy love and power.

3. All for Jesus – at Thine altar
   Thou wilt give us sweet content;
   there, dear Lord, we shall receive Thee
   in the solemn Sacrament.

4. All for Jesus – Thou hast loved us;
   all for Jesus – Thou hast died;
   all for Jesus – Thou art with us;
   all for Jesus Crucified.

5. All for Jesus – all for Jesus,
   this the Church's song must be;
   till, at last, her sons are gathered
   one in love and one in Thee.

Words: W.J.Sparrow-Simpson

© Novello & Co Ltd

Music: J.Stainer
      adapted for use in complete
      Celebration Hymnal by Roger Humphrey

© 1984 Mayhew–McCrimmon Ltd

389 MICHAEL (87.87.33.7)

1. All my hope on God is foun- ded; he doth still my

trust re- new. Me through change and chance he guid- eth, on- ly

good and on- ly true. God un- known, he a- lone calls my

heart to be his own.

2. Pride of man and earthly glory,
   sword and crown betray God's trust;
   what with lavish care man buildeth,
   tower and temple, fall to dust.
   But God's power, hour by hour,
   is my temple and my tower.

3. God's great goodness ay endureth,
   deep his wisdom, passing thought:
   splendour, light, and life attend him,
   beauty springeth out of nought.
   Evermore, from his store
   new-born worlds rise and adore.

4. Still from man to God eternal
   sacrifice of praise be done,
   high above all praises praising
   for the gift of Christ his Son.
   Christ doth call one and all:
   Ye who follow shall not fall.

Words: J. Neander 1650–80, paraphrased
       by R.S. Bridges 1844–1930
Music: Herbert Howells

© Novello & Co.

Refrain

All the earth pro - claim the Lord, sing your praise to God. *Fine*

Verse

Serve you the Lord, hearts filled with glad - ness. Come into his pre-sence singing joy. *for* **D.C.**

Refrain for mixed voices

S A

T B

2. Know that the Lord is our creator.
   Yes, he is our Father; we are his sons.

3. We are the sheep of his green pasture,
   for we are his people; he is our God.

4. Enter his gates bringing thanksgiving,
   O enter his courts while singing his praise.

5. Our Lord is good, his love enduring,
   his word is abiding now with all men.

6. Honour and praise be to the Father,
   the Son, and the Spirit, world without end.

Words: based on Psalm 100
by Lucien Deiss
Music: Lucien Deiss

391

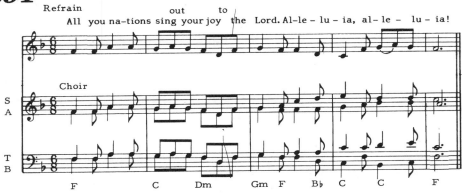

Refrain
All you na-tions sing your joy out to the Lord. Al-le – lu – ia, al-le – lu – ia!

Choir

F   C   Dm   Gm   F   Bb   C   C   F

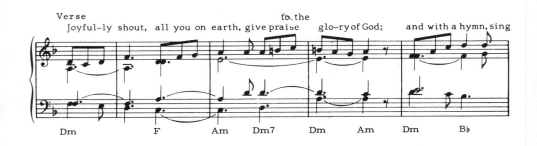

Verse
Joyful-ly shout, all you on earth, give praise to the glo-ry of God; and with a hymn, sing

Dm   F   Am   Dm7   Dm   Am   Dm   Bb

out his glor-i-ous praise: Al –le – lu – ia!

Am   Bbmaj7   Gm   F   C   Dm

All you nations, sing out your joy in the Lord:
Alleluia, alleluia!

1. Joyfully shout, all you on earth,
    give praise to the glory of God;
    and with a hymn, sing out his glorious praise:
    Alleluia!

2. Lift up your hearts, sing to your God:
    tremendous his deeds among men!
    vanquished your foes, struck down by power and might:
    Alleluia!

3. Let all the earth kneel in his sight,
    extolling his marvellous fame;
    honour his name, in highest heaven give praise:
    Alleluia!

4. Come forth and see all the great works
    that God has brought forth by his might;
    fall on your knees before his glorious throne:
    Alleluia!

5. Parting the seas with might and pow'r,
    he rescued his people from shame;
    let us give thanks for all his merciful deeds:
    Alleluia!

6. His eyes keep watch on all the earth,
    his strength is forever renewed;
    and let no man rebel against his commands:
    Alleluia!

7. Tested are we by God the Lord,
    as silver is tested by fire;
    burdened with pain, we fall ensnared in our sins:
    Alleluia!

8. Over our heads wicked men rode,
    we passed through the fire and the flood;
    then, Lord, you brought your people into your peace:
    Alleluia!

9. Glory and thanks be to the Father;
    honour and praise to the Son;
    and to the spirit, source of life and of love:
    Alleluia!

Words: based on Psalm 66
by Lucien Deiss
Music: Lucien Deiss

392

Alleluia, alleluia, alleluia,
Jesus is alive!

1. Praise the Lord for
   he is good eternally,
   and his loving kindness
   for us never fails.

2. His strong right hand
   overcomes and lifts us up;
   I'll never die, but live
   to praise his power to save.

3. For the stone rejected
   by the builder's sin
   has become the cornerstone
   of God's new House.

4. And he gives us the light
   wherewith to see;
   his intention is
   that we should live with him.

Based on Psalm 117/8

393   *Same tune as above.*

Alleluia, alleluia, alleluia,
may God's Spirit come!

1. Bless the Lord, my soul,
   for he is great and good:
   earth he has enriched
   with all his mighty works.

2. You send forth your Spirit,
   then creation starts,
   and you still renew
   all things upon the earth.

3. May the Lord find joy
   in all that he creates;
   and my thoughts about him
   fill my heart with joy.

Based on Psalm 103/4

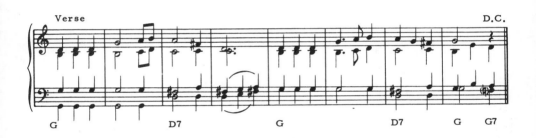

Alleluia! Alleluia! Alleluia, sons of God, arise.
Alleluia! Alleluia! sons of God arise and follow the Lord.

1. Come and be clothed in his righteousness;
   come join the band who are called by his name.

2. Look at the world which is bound by sin;
   walk into the midst of it proclaiming my life.

Words and music: Mimi Farra

© 1971, 1975 Celebration Services (International) Ltd

Harmony: for Celebration Hymnal
by John Rombaut

© 1981 Mayhew-McCrimmon Ltd

395

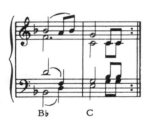

Alleluia, alleluia, give thanks to the risen Lord.
Alleluia, alleluia, give praise to his name.

1. Jesus is Lord of all the earth.
   He is the King of creation.

2. Spread the good news o'er all the earth.
   Jesus has died and has risen.

3. We have been crucified with Christ.
   Now we shall live for ever.

4. God has proclaimed the just reward.
   Life for all men, alleluia.

5. Come, let us praise the living God,
   joyfully sing to our Saviour.

Words and music: Don Fishel

Harmony: for Celebration Hymnal
         by Eric Welch
         by permission of The Word of God

396

Refrain

Al – le – lu – ia, al – le – lu – ia!

Verse 1

1. Sal va tion and glory and pow'r be-long to our God,

Semi-chorus   To refrain

al – le – lu – ia! His judge-ments are true and just.

Verse 2

2. Praise our God, all you his ser – vants,

Semi-chorus

To refrain

al – le-lu – ia! You who fear him great and small

Verse 3

3. The Lord our God, the al – migh – ty, reigns,

Semi-chorus

al – le-lu –ia! let us re- joice and e- xult and give him the Glory

Refrain

Al – le – lu – ia, al – le – lu – ia!

Verse 4

4. The mar – riage of the Lamb has come,

Semi chorus.

al – le–lu – ia! and his Bride has made her–self rea – dy.

To refrain

Words: based on Revelation 19:1-2,5-7
by P.G. Fitzpatrick
Music: P.G. Fitzpatrick

© P.G. Fitzpatrick

397

NETHERLANDS (12 12.12 12)

1. Al- migh- ty Fa- ther, who for us thy Son didst

give, that men and na- tions through his pre-cious death might live,

(small notes organ only)

in mer- cy guard us, lest by sloth and self-ish pride we

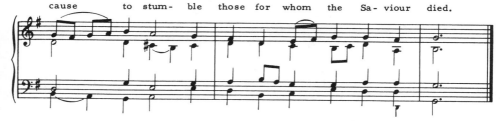

cause to stum- ble those for whom the Sa- viour died.

2. We are thy stewards; thine our talents, wisdom, skill;
   our only glory that we may thy trust fulfill;
   that we thy pleasure in our neighbour's good pursue,
   if thou but workest in us both to will and do.

3. On just and unjust thou thy care dost freely shower;
   make us, thy children, free from greed and lust for power,
   lest human justice, yoked with man's unequal laws,
   oppress the needy and neglect the humble cause.

4. Let not thy worship blind us to the claims of love;
   but let thy manna lead us to the feast above,
   to seek the country which by faith we now possess,
   where Christ, our treasure, reigns in peace and righteousness.

Words: George B. Caird (b.1917) © United Reformed Church
Music: 16th Century melody, as given by A. Valerius in his 'Nederlandstsche
       Gedenck-Clanck, (1626). Harmonised by John Wilson. © Oxford University Press

ANGEL VOICES   (85.85.87)

1. Angel-voices ever singing
   round thy throne of light,
   angel-harps for ever ringing,
   rest not day nor night;
   thousands only live to bless thee
   and confess thee Lord of might.

2. Thou who art beyond the farthest
   mortal eye can scan,
   can it be that thou regardest
   songs of sinful man?
   Can we know that thou art near us,
   and wilt hear us? Yes, we can.

3. Yes, we know that thou rejoicest
   o'er each work of thine;
   thou didst ears and hands and voices
   for thy praise design;
   craftsman's art and music's measure
   for thy pleasure all combine.

4. In thy house, great God, we offer
   of thine own to thee;
   and for thine acceptance proffer
   all unworthily.
   Hearts and minds and hands and voices
   in our choicest psalmody.

5. Honour, glory, might, and merit
   thine shall ever be,
   Father, Son, and Holy Spirit,
   Blessed Trinity!
   Of the best that thou hast given
   earth and heaven render thee.

Words: F. Pott
Music: E.G. Monk, 1819-1900

399 FOLKSONG (WALY WALY)   (98.98)

Organ Introduction
to Verses 1 & 4

1. An Up- per

mp

senza Ped.

Room did our Lord pre- pare for those he loved un- til the end:

Unison*

Ped. ad lib.

And his dis- ci- ples still ga- ther there, to ce- le-

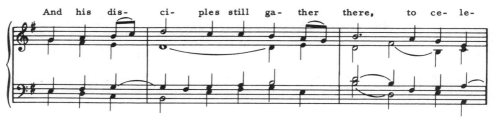

brate their Ri- sen Friend.

Words: F. Pratt Green (b.1903)
Music: English Traditional Melody,
   arranged by John Wilson

Words © Stainer & Bell Ltd.
Music © Oxford University Press

* If any of Verses 1 - 3 are sung by the Choir alone, they may be in Harmony, with
  A. T. B. humming or singing a vowel sound; but Verse 4 should always be in Unison.

2. A lasting gift Jesus gave his own:
   To share his bread, his loving cup.
   Whatever burdens may bow us down,
   He by his cross shall lift us up.

3. And after Supper he washed their feet,
   for service, too, is sacrament.
   In him our joy shall be made complete -
   sent out to serve, as he was sent.

Organ introduction -

4. No end there is! We depart in peace.
   He loves beyond our uttermost:
   In every room in our Father's house
   He will be there, as Lord and Host.

1. As earth that is dry and parched in the sun
   lies waiting for rain,
   my soul is a desert, arid and waste;
   it longs for your Word, O Lord.

   Come to the waters, all you who thirst;
   come now, and eat my bread.

2. Though you have no money, come, buy my corn
   and drink my red wine.
   Why spend precious gold on what will not last?
   Hear me, and your soul will live.

3. As one on a journey strays from the road
   and falls in the dark,
   my mind is a wanderer, choosing wrong paths
   and longing to find a star.

4. The Lord is your light, the Lord is your strength;
   turn back to him now.
   For his ways are not the ways you would choose,
   and his thoughts are always new.

5. As rain from the mountains falls on the land
   and brings forth the seed,
   the word of the Lord sinks deep in our hearts,
   creating the flower of truth.

Words: Isaiah 55
            paraphrased by Anne Conway
Music: Anne Conway

401

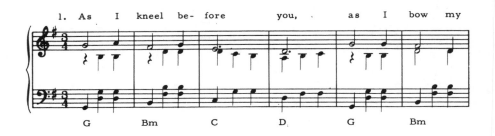

1. As I kneel be- fore you, as I bow my

G   Bm   C   D   G   Bm

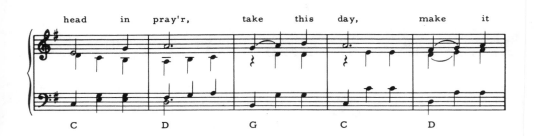

head in pray'r, take this day, make it

C   D   G   C   D

yours and fill me with your love.

G   C   D   G

Chorus*

A- ve, Ma- ri- a, gra- ti- a

Bm   C   D7   G   Bm

* The lower notes are the tune.

ple-   na,   Do-   mi-   nus   te-

C   D   G   C   D

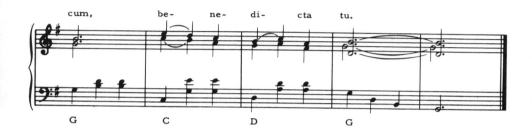

cum,   be-   ne-   di-   cta   tu.

G   C   D   G

2. All I have I give you,
      ev'ry dream and wish are yours.
      Mother of Christ, Mother of mine,
      present them to my Lord.

3. As I kneel before you,
      and I see your smiling face,
      ev'ry thought, ev'ry word
      is lost in your embrace.

Words and Music: Maria Parkinson

402

LES COMMANDEMENTS DE DIEU   (98.98)

1. As long as men on earth are liv- ing, and trees are yield-ing

fruits on earth, you are our Fa- ther. Thanks we

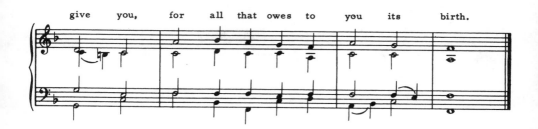

give you, for all that owes to you its birth.

2. You are our light and life and Saviour,
   you rescue us when we are dead.
   You gave your Son to be our neighbour.
   He feeds us with his living bread.

3. As long as human words are spoken
   and for each other we exist,
   your steadfastness remains unbroken;
   for Jesus' sake, your name be blessed.

4. You are the one who clothes the flowers,
   you feed the birds in all the land.
   You are our shelter: all my hours
   and all my days are in your hand.

5. Therefore, let all the world adore you.
   It is your love that brought it forth.
   You live among us, we before you.
   Your offspring are we. Praise the Lord!

Words: Huub Oosterhuis and C.M.DeVries
Music: Original form of melody by Louis Bourgeois c. 1510-c. 1561
       from the 'Genevan Psalter', 1543

403

Refrain

As one bo – dy we are wed by par – tak – ing

of the self – same Bread; and Je – sus Christ of that bo – dy is the

head: the ho – ly Church of God.

Verses

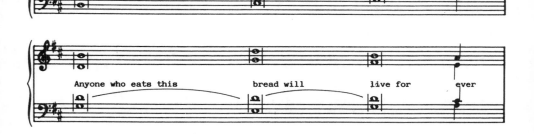

1. I am the living bread which has come down from heaven.

Anyone who eats this bread will live for ever

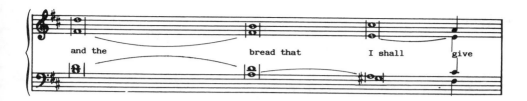

and the   bread that   I shall   give

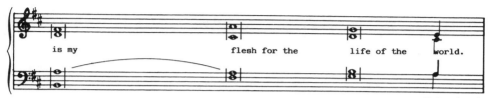

is my   flesh for the   life of the   world.

(John 6:51)

2. On the same night that he was betrayed, the Lord Jesus took some bread, thanked God for it, and broke it, and said: 'This is my body, which is given up for you. Do this in memory of me.' *(1 Cor.11:23b-24)*

3. In the same way after supper he took the cup and said: 'This cup is the new covenant in my blood. Do this in memory of me.' So doing, we proclaim his death, until he comes again. *(1 Cor.11:25-26)*

4. Just as a human body, though it is made up of many parts, these parts though many, make one body. In the one Spirit we were all baptised, one Spirit given to us all to drink. *(1 Cor.11:12-13)*

5. There is one body, there is one Spirit just as we were called into one and the same hope. There is one Lord, one faith, one baptism and one God, who is Father over all. *(Ephesians 4:4-6)*

Words, from Scripture: Jean-Paul Lecot, W.R.Lawrence, R.B.Kelly
Music: Jean-Paul Lecot

English language rights © 1984 Kevin Mayhew Ltd,
55 Leigh Road, Leigh-on-Sea, Essex SS9 1JB

Verse harmony for Celebration Hymnal by Steven Foster © 1984 Mayhew-McCrimmon Ltd

A - Unison throughout

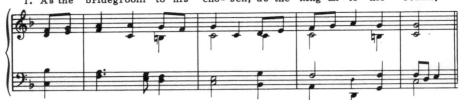

1. As the bridegroom to his cho-sen, as the king un-to his realm,

B

as the keep un- to the ca-stle, as the pi-lot to the helm,

All

so, Lord, art thou to me.

A and B may be sung by contrasted groups of voices

2. As the fountain in the garden,
   as the candle in the dark,
   as the treasure in the coffer,
   as the manna in the ark,
   So, Lord, art thou to me.

3. As the music at the banquet,
   as the stamp unto the seal,
   as the medicine to the fainting,
   as the wine-cup at the meal,
   so, Lord, art thou to me.

4. As the ruby in the setting,
   as the honey in the comb,
   as the light within the lantern,
   as the father in the home,
   so, Lord, art thou to me.

5. As the sunshine in the heavens,
   as the image in the glass,
   as the fruit unto the fig-tree,
   as the dew unto the grass,
   so, Lord, art thou to me.

Words: Par. from (?) John Tauler (1300–61)
    by Emma Frances Bevan (1827–1909)
Music: Peter Cutts (b.1937)

1. A-wake, a-wake: fling off the night! For God has

sent his glo-rious light; and we who live in Christ's new

day must works of dark-ness put a-way.

Another setting of this hymn (in C) will be found at No.332

2. Awake and rise, like men renewed,
   men with the Spirit's power endued.
   The light of life in us must glow,
   and fruits of truth and goodness show.

3. Let in the light; all sin expose
   to Christ, whose life no darkness knows.
   Before his cross for guidance kneel;
   his light will judge and, judging, heal.

4. Awake, and rise up from the dead,
   and Christ his light on you will shed.
   Its power will wrong desires destroy,
   and your whole nature fill with joy.

5. Then sing for joy, and use each day;
   give thanks for everything alway.
   Lift up your hearts; with one accord
   praise God through Jesus Christ our Lord.

Words: J.R. Peacey 1896–1971, based on Ephesians 5:6–20
Music: Melody from the Grenoble Antiphoners of 1753 and 1868.
     Harmony by Redmund Shaw

Words © Mildred Peacey
Arrangement © Paul Inwood

406 a

C   F   Dm   G7   C   C7   F   C

Dm   G7   Dm7   G   C   G7   Am   C   F   Dm   G7   C

Music: Joan McCrimmon
Harmony: Eric Welch

©   1980, 1981 Mayhew-McCrimmon Ltd

406 b

Am   Em7   Am   Em7   Am   Em7

Am   Em7   Am   Em   F   G   C   Dm7

F   E   D   F   A   C

Em   Dm   C   G   Am7   G

1. "Bartimaeus, Bartimaeus,
   do you hear them, do you know?
   They have seen the prophet Jesus
   in the streets of Jericho.
   Bartimaeus, it is he!
   What a shame you cannot see."

2. "Son of David, Son of David
   walking in the blessed light,
   I a beggar ask no money.
   Lord, may I receive my sight?
   Son of David, pity me.
   You have power to make me see."

3. "Bartimaeus, Bartimaeus,
   you have eyes to know your need;
   you have eyes to know the Giver;
   surely this is sight indeed!
   Bartimaeus, come to me.
   Bartimaeus, you shall see."

4. Son of David, Son of David
   kindle in the human soul.
   one blind faith like Bartimaeus;
   call us out, and make us whole.
   Son of David, source of light,
   Lord, may we receive our sight?

Music: Bill Tamblyn

© 1980 Bill Tamblyn

Words: Michael Hewlett

© 1980 Michael Hewlett

407 FINLANDIA (10.10.10.10.10.10)

1. Be still, my soul: the Lord
      is on your side;
   bear patiently the cross
      of grief and pain;
   leave to your God
      to order and provide;
   in every change
      he faithful will remain.
   Be still, my soul: your best
      your. heavenly friend
   through thorny ways
      leads to a joyful end.

2. Be still, my soul:
      your God will undertake
   to guide the future
      as he has the past.
   Your hope, your confidence
      let nothing shake,
   all now mysterious
      shall be clear at last.
   Be still, my soul:
      the tempests still obey
   his voice, who ruled them
      once on Galilee.

3. Be still, my soul:
      the hour is hastening on
   when we shall be for ever
      with the Lord,
   when disappointment, grief
      and fear are gone,
   sorrow forgotten,
      love's pure joy restored.
   Be still, my soul:
      when change and tears are past,
   all safe and blessed
      we shall meet at last.

Words: Katharina von Schlegel
      translated by Jane L. Borthwick (1813–1897)
      revised by Australian Hymn Book Committee
Music: Jean Sibelius (1865–1957)
      from 'Finlandia'

Music © Breitkopf and Hartel, Wiesbaden

1. Before Christ died he took some bread,
   and then he took some wine.
   "My body and my blood," he said,
   "a sacrificial sign."

2. "Now eat and drink, I am your food.
   I promise you will see
   your lives transformed, your hearts renewed;
   you'll die and live with me."

3. We drink this wine, we eat this bread,
   as Jesus bade us do.
   The covenant for which he bled
   today we must renew.

4. By faith, in broken bread we see
   the body of our Lord.
   By faith, we know the wine to be
   his holy blood outpoured.

5. Each time the church, for memory's sake,
   repeats Christ's holy act,
   each time we of that meal partake,
   Christ's death we re-enact.

6. From sunrise to the setting sun
   this death we will proclaim.
   Each day Christ promises to come
   until he comes again.

Words: Peter de Rosa
Music: Eric Welch

Words & Music © 1970, 1980 Mayhew—McCrimmon Ltd

409

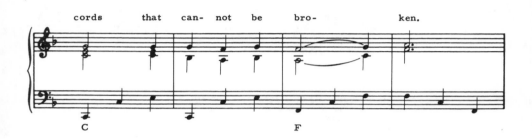

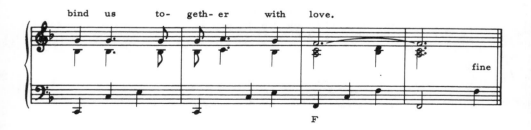

Verse

There is on-ly one God.

There is on-ly one King.

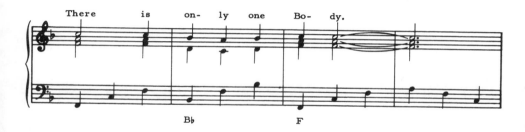

There is on-ly one Bo-dy.

That is why we sing.

D.C. al fine

2. Made for the glory of God,
   purchased by his precious Son.
   Born with the right to be clean,
   for Jesus the victory has won . . .

3. You are the family of God.
   You are the promise divine.
   You are God's chosen desire.
   You are the glorious new wine . . .

Words and Music: B. Gillman.

© 1977 by Thankyou Music, Eastbourne.

410

Verse

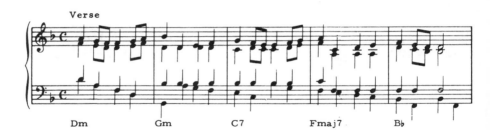

Dm   Gm   C7   Fmaj7   B♭

Refrain

Dm   Fdim   A7   D7   Gm   C7   F7   B♭

Gm   A   Dm   D7   Gm   C7   F7   B♭   Gm   A7   Dm (D)

1. Blest are you, Lord,
    God of all creation,
   thanks to your goodness
    this bread we offer:
   fruit of the earth,
    work of our hands,
   it will become
    the bread of life.

2. Blest are you, Lord,
    God of all creation,
   thanks to your goodness
    this wine we offer:
   fruit of the earth,
    work of our hands,
   it will become
    the cup of life.

Blessed be God! Blessed be God!
Blessed be God forever! Amen!
Blessed be God! Blessed be God!
Blessed be God forever! Amen!

Words and music: Aniceto Nazareth

ⓒ Aniceto Nazareth

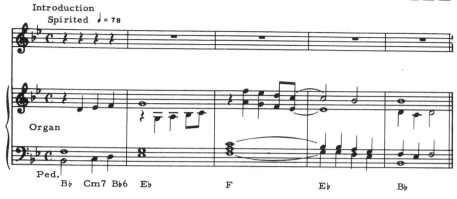

Introduction
Spirited ♩ = 78

Organ

Ped.

Bb   Cm7 Bb6   Eb   F   Eb   Bb

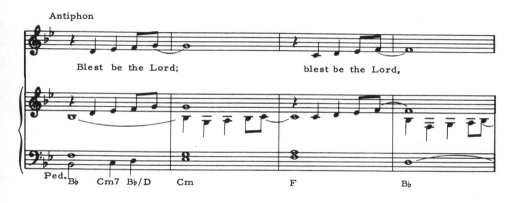

Antiphon

Blest be the Lord;   blest be the Lord,

Ped. Bb   Cm7 Bb/D Cm   F   Bb

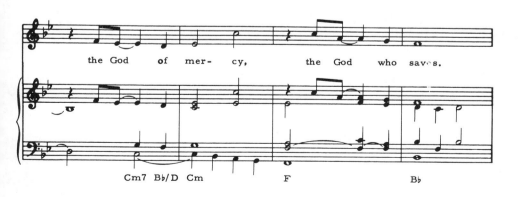

the God   of   mer- cy,   the God   who saves.

Cm7 Bb/D Cm   F   Bb

He will pro-tect me from their wick-ed hands.

Bb   F   Eb   Bb

Be-neath the shad-ow of his wings I will rejoice

Eb   F   Eb

to find a dwell-ing place se-cure.

Bb   F   Eb   Bb

2. I need not shrink before
the terrors of the night,
nor stand alone before
the light of day.
No harm shall come to me,
no arrow strike me down,
no evil settle in my soul.

3. Although a thousand strong
have fallen at my side,
I'll not be shaken with
the Lord at hand.
His faithful love is all
the armour that I need
to wage my battle with the foe.

Words: Based on Psalm (90)91, by Dan Schutte, S.J.
Music: Dan Schutte, arranged by Sr. Theophane Hytrek, O.S.F.

412

WEISSE (98.98)   Slow and dignified

Bread of the world in mer - cy bro-ken, wine of the soul in

mer - cy shed, by whom the words of life were spo - ken,

and in whose death our sins are dead.

2. Look on the heart by sorrow broken,
look on the tears by sinners shed;
and be your feast to us the token
that by your grace our souls are fed.

Words: Reginald Heber (1783-1826)
Music: Source unknown,
harmonised by J.S. Bach

413

1. Break not the circle of enabling love,
    where people grow, forgiven and forgiving;
    break not that circle, make it wider still,
    till it includes, embraces all the living.

2. Come, wonder at this love that comes to life,
    where words of freedom are with humour spoken
    and people keep no score of wrong and guilt,
    but will that human bonds remain unbroken.

3. Come, wonder at the Lord who came and comes
    to teach the world the craft of hopeful craving
    for peace and wholeness that will fill the earth:
    he calls his people to creative living.

4. Join then the movement of the love that frees,
    till people of whatever race or nation,
    will truly be themselves, stand on their feet,
    see eye to eye with laughter and elation.

Words : Fred Kaan
Music: Doreen Potter

414

Am7   Dsus4/A

                        Am7

Dsus4/A

Refrain

Breathing the words   of   hum-ble o - be –   dience true ———

Am7   Dsus4/A

Let it be so,   and let it be done for

Am7

you ———————————————————— .   I ———— am the

Dsus4/A   Cmaj7

hand–maid   of the Lord ———————————————— .

Gsus4   G   A   A4   A

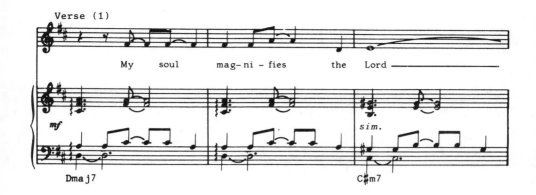

Verse (1)

My soul mag-ni – fies the Lord ———

Dmaj7   C#m7

mf   *sim.*

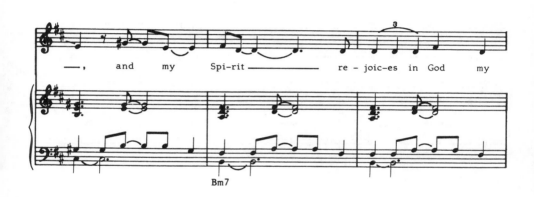

——, and my Spi-rit ——— re – joic-es in God my

Bm7

King ———— .   Hence-forth ——— all

A   Asus4   Dmaj7

men will call me bles – sed ————————, be–cause my

C#m7

God ———————— has done great things for me ————————

Bm7   Cmaj7   G6/B

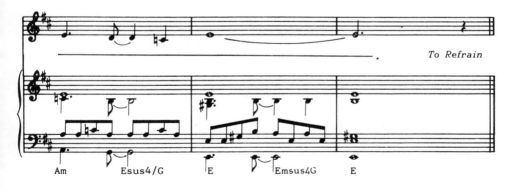

To Refrain

Am   Esus4/G   E   Emsus4G   E

2. His mer - cy ———— spans ge - ne - ra - tions,——
3. The migh - ty ———— flung from —— their thrones ————
4. In all his ———— mer - cy he ———— has helped ————
5. Give praise to —— the Fa - ther —— Al - migh - ty,——

2. —— for those —— who fear him, ———— ho - ly ———— is his
3. ———————— and —— ex - al - ted ———————————— the low -
4. ———————— Is - ra - el ———————— the home ———— of our
5. ———————— to his Son,——————————— Je - sus —— Christ our

2. name,——————— He has shown —— the might —— of —— his —— arm.—
3. - ly. ———————— He has filled —— the hun-gry— with —— good —— things.
4. fa - thers. —— As he cared ——————————— for — A - bra - ham,—
5. Lord. ———————— To the Spi - rit —— who dwells —— in —— our —— hearts,

2. —— The proud he's scattered ———————————— in their con -
3. —— The rich he's sent ——————— emp - ty hand - ed —— a -
4. ———— so —— he —— cares for us ——————— un - til the
5. ———— now and— for— e - ver. ———————————— A -

2. - ceit. _____
3. - way. _____
4. - end. _____
5. - men. _____

Words and Music: Liz Powell/Jean Henriot
Transcribed by Andrew Wright

© 1984 Mayhew-McCrimmon Ltd

415

Gently

1. Bright star of morning dawn on our darkness, Jesus our Master, our Lord and King, our hearts we give you now and forever, all that we care for to you we bring.

D7 G Em E7 Am D7 G Em E7 Am D7 G

2. All of life's troubles, each daily burden
are eased and lightened when you are near.
Help us to stay close, trusting and child-like,
calmed by your presence and free from fear.

3. Immortal Saviour forgive our weakness,
for you have known, Lord, our frailty.
May we walk with you, safe in your love-light,
each day and until eternity.

Words and Music: Estelle White
© Mayhew-McCrimmon Ltd

416

Moderato

Verses 1.-2.

Eb   Ab Eb   Ab Eb   Ab Eb   Ab   Eb

1. Bro – ther   Sun   and Sis – ter   Moon,
2. Bro – ther   Wind   and Sis – ter   Air,

Eb

I   sel–dom hear   you,   sel – dom hear your tune.
O – pen my eyes   to   vi–sions pure and fair

Ab   Bb7   Eb

Cm   Ab   Gm   Ab   Bb7   Eb

Pre – oc–cu–pied   with sel–fish mi – se–ry.
that I may see   the glo–ry a – round me.

Cm   Ab   Gm   Fm7   Bb7   Eb

Fm7   Bb7   Eb

I   am God's crea – ture,   of him   I am

Eb   Ab   Gm   Fm   Bb7

part.   I   feel his   love   a – wa – ke–ning my

Eb   Ab   Gm   Fm   Fm7

heart.   3.   Bro – ther Sun   and
Verse 3.

Ab/Bb   Bb7   Eb

Sis – ter   Moon   now   do   I   see   you,

Ab   Bb7   Eb   Cm   Ab   Gm

I   can hear your tune,   so   much in lo – ve with

Fm   Bb   Eb   Cm   Ab   Gm

all   I   sur – vey.

Fm7   Bb7   Ab   Eb   Bb7   Eb

Words : based on Francis of Assisi
by Donovan
Music: Donovan

© 1973 Famous Music Corporation (Famous Chappell)

417

Gently

1. But I say un- to you, love your en- e- mies and pray for those who hurt you. Give to those who ask, don't turn a- way. And be like your Fa- ther in hea- ven a- bove who caus- es his sun to shine on e- vil and good, and sends down his rain

Refrain

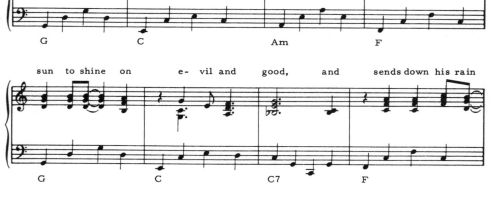

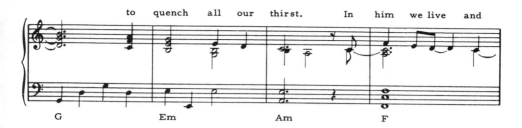

to quench all our thirst. In him we live and

G　　Em　　Am　　F

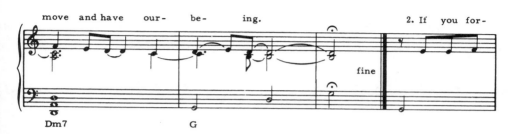

move and have our- be- ing.　　2. If you for-

fine

Dm7　　G

give each oth- er, so will God for- give you.

C　　F　　G

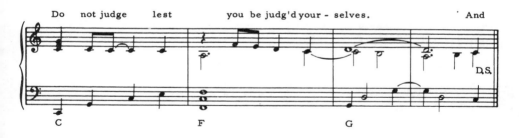

Do not judge lest you be judg'd your-selves. And

D.S.

C　　F　　G

3. When you see the hungry,
   feed them from your table.
   For the poor and weary,
   be their wat'ring place.
   And

Words and Music: Beverlee Paine

418

Refrain

Fine

Am   C   Dm7   E

By his wounds we have been healed.

Where a bar is empty, it has to be omitted completely: the accompanist must also omit the equivalent bars in his part.

Verses

1. 1. Christ suf-fer'd for you,

2. 2. He com-mit-ted no sin; no guile was found on his lips.

3. 3. When he suf-fer'd he did not threa-ten;

4. 4. He him-self bore our sins in his bo-dy on the tree, that

5. 5. For you were stra-ying like sheep, but now have re-turned to the

Am   Dm   Am   Am7   Am   Dm   Am

lea-ving you an e-xam-ple that you should fol-low in his steps.

when he was re- -viled, he did not re-vile in re-turn.

but he trus-ted in him who jud-ges just - ly.

we might die to sin and live to righ-teous-ness.

shep-herd and guardian of your souls.

F G Am Am7 C Dm Em

Words: 1 Peter 2:21-24
Music: Joseph Walshe

Harmony: for Celebration Hymnal
by Frances M. & Robert B. Kelly

© Joseph Walshe

© 1981 Mayhew-McCrimmon Ltd

419

1. By the Cross which did to death our on-ly Sa-viour, this

bles-sed vine from which grapes are gathered in: Je-sus Christ, we

(Choir)

thank and bless you. By the Cross which casts down fire upon our

pla-net, this liv-ing branch which can heal our ev'-ry sin: Je-sus

Christ, we glo - ri - fy you. By the Cross on Calv'ry's
hill se - cure - ly plan - ted, this liv - ing branch which can heal our ev'ry
sin: Conqu'ring God, we your Church pro - claim you.

(Choir)

2. By the Blood with which we marked the wooden lintels
    for our protection the night when God passed by:
    Jesus Christ, we thank and bless you.
    By the Blood which in our Exodus once saved us,
    when hell was sealed up by God's engulfing sea:
    Jesus Christ, we glorify you.
    By the Blood which kills the poison in bad fruitage,
    and gives new life to the dead sap in the tree:
    conquering God, we your Church proclaim you!

3. By the Death on Calv'ry's hill of him the First-born,
who bears the wood and the flame for his own pyre:
Jesus Christ, we thank and bless you.
By the Death, amid the thorns, of God's own Shepherd,
the Paschal Lamb who was pierced by our despair:
Jesus Christ, we glorify you.
By the Death of God's belov'd outside his vineyard,
that he might change us from murd'rer into heir:
conquering God, we your Church proclaim you!

4. By the Wood which sings a song of nuptial gladness,
of God who takes for his bride our human race:
Jesus Christ, we thank and bless you.
By the Wood which raises up in his full vigour
the Son of Man who draws all men by his grace:
Jesus Christ, we glorify you.
By the Wood where he perfects his royal Priesthood
in one High Priest who for sin is sacrifice:
conquering God, we your Church proclaim you!

5. Holy Tree which reaches up from earth to heaven
that all the world may exult in Jacob's God:
Jesus Christ, we thank and bless you.
Mighty Ship which snatches us from God's deep anger,
saves us, with Noah, from drowning in the Flood:
Jesus Christ, we glorify you.
Tender Wood which gives to brackish water sweetness,
and from the Rock shall strike fountains for our food:
conquering God, we your Church proclaim you!

Words: Didier Rimaud
        translated by F. Pratt Green
Music: Joseph Gelineau

Words © Stainer & Bell Ltd
Music © SEFIM (H67/1)

420

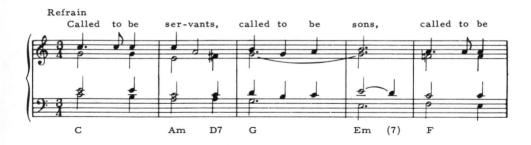

Called to be ser-vants, called to be sons, called to be

C   Am   D7   G   Em   (7)   F

daugh-ters, we're called to be one. Called in- to ser-vice,

Dm7   G7   C   Dm7   E(sus4)   Dm   C

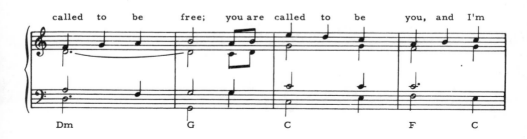

called to be free; you are called to be you, and I'm

Dm   G   C   F   C

Last time only | Verse

called to be me.   1. Chil-dren, come with wide o- pen

Dm7   G7(sus4)   C   C   Am   D7   G

eyes. Look   at   the   wa-ter; you   have been bap- tised. You're

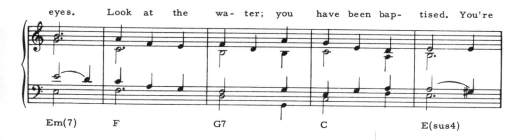

Em(7)   F   G7   C   E(sus4)

free from the slav'-ry that   bound you   to   sin, so live now as

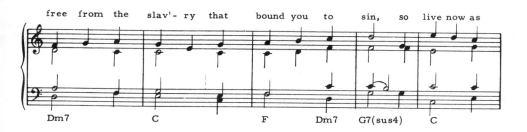

Dm7   C   F   Dm7 G7(sus4)   C

chil-dren in the king-dom   of   heav'n.

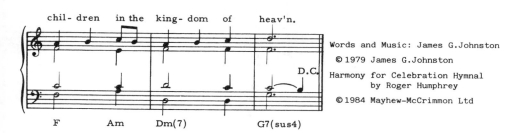

D.C.

F   Am   Dm(7)   G7(sus4)

Words and Music: James G.Johnston

© 1979 James G.Johnston

Harmony for Celebration Hymnal
    by Roger Humphrey

© 1984 Mayhew-McCrimmon Ltd

2. We are saints! Forgiveness is sure –
    not of ourselves, but the cross Christ endured.
    We're free from the Law that said "You must provide!"
    We're free to be servants; we're called; we're baptised.

3. Jesus closed the dark pit of death.
    He has breathed on us with his holy breath.
    He gives us the faith to respond to his News.
    We're free to show mercy, to love, to be bruised.

421

BUNESSAN   55 53 D

C   Am Dm   G   Dm   G   Am   C   Am C   Dm   G

C   Am   Dm   C   F   Dm   C   Em   Am   G7   C

1. Child in the manger, infant of Mary;
   outcast and stranger Lord of all;
   child who inherits all our transgressions,
   all our demerits on him fall.

2. Once the most holy child of salvation
   gently and lowly lived below;
   now as our glorious mighty Redeemer,
   see him victorious o'er each foe.

3. Prophets foretold him, infant of wonder;
   angels behold him on his throne;
   worthy our Saviour of all their praises;
   happy for ever are his own.

Words : Mary Macdonald
        translated by Lachlan Macbean
Music : Traditional Gaelic

422

G   D7   G   C   Am   D   Bm   G   A   Bm Em   A7

D G C Em C Bm Am E7 Am E7 Am Am6 B7

Em D Am D G D7 G A Bm A7 D Em7 F♯7 Bm G D7

G Em Am C D7 E7 Am C+ Am G D G

1. Christ be my way, my path to find the Father,
    my guide when there's no trusting sound or sight;
    Christ fill my mind to cleanse the understanding,
    to be my truth, a beacon blazing bright;
    Christ all I hope for, strengthening, upholding,
    my breath of life, my pride and my delight.

    Truth on my tongue,
       his way to guide my walking
    and I shall live,
       not I but Christ in me!

2. No way but Christ, his cross the only signpost
    and he our road through death to blessedness;
    no safety else, no footing for the pilgrim,
    without his leading there's no guide nor guess:
    our way to where the Father waits in welcome
    to greet us home from night and wilderness.

3. We name him Lord, Truth rising like a tower
    above the world his coming shook and stirred:
    truth born in time, a child, and shown to shepherds
    when God's great glory on the hills was heard:
    truth born beyond all time, when first the Father
    pronounced his mighty all-creating Word.

4. Christ, Life of man, creation's mind and maker,
    hid deep in God before the world began,
    God born of God, the everlasting mercy,
    the Father's love, who stopped and put on man:
    man's life that ebbed beneath the nails, the crowning,
    then burst in one white dawn death's narrow span.

Words: Luke Connaughton
Music: Anthony Milner

Words © 1979 Mayhew-McCrimmon
                                 Ltd
Music © 1979 Anthony Milner

423

Verse

Refrain

1. Christ has arisen. Alleluia!
   Rejoice and praise him; alleluia!
   For our Redeemer burst
   from the tomb,
   even from death, dispelling
   its gloom.

   Let us sing praise to him
   with endless joy.
   Death's fearful sting he has
   come to destroy.
   Our sins forgiving, alleluia!
   Jesus is living, alleluia!

2. For three long days the grave
   did its worst,
   until its strength by God
   was dispersed.
   He who gives life
   did death undergo,
   and in its conquest
   his might did show.

3. The angel said to them,
   'Do not fear,
   you look for Jesus who is not here.
   See for yourselves, the tomb is
   all bare:
   only the grave-clothes are
   lying there.'

4. Go spread the news, he's not
   in the grave.
   He has arisen, mankind to save.
   Jesus' redeeming labours are done.
   Even the battle with sin is won.

Words: translated from Swahili
       by Howard S. Olsen
Music: Haya traditional melody (Tanzania)

©1977 Augsburg Publishing House

Harmony: for Celebration Hymnal
         by Frances M. & Robert B. Kelly

©1981 Mayhew-McCrimmon Ltd

Another harmonization will be found
at No.486.

1. Christ is alive, with joy we sing;
   we celebrate our risen Lord,
   praising the glory of his name.
   Alleluia, alleluia, alleluia.

2. He is the grain of wheat that died;
   sown in distress and reaped in joy,
   yielding a harvest of new life.
   Alleluia, alleluia, alleluia.

3. He is the sun which brings the dawn:
   he is the light of all the world,
   setting us free from death and sin.
   Alleluia, alleluia, alleluia.

4. He is the vine set in the earth,
   sharing our life, becoming man,
   that man might share in God's own life.
   Alleluia, alleluia, alleluia.

5. Christ is alive, with joy we sing;
   we celebrate our risen Lord,
   praising the glory of his name.
   Alleluia, alleluia, alleluia.

Words: Pamela Stotter
Music: Melchior Vulpius (1560-1615)

Words   © 1979 Pamela Stotter

425

(Optional repeat)

Words: Anonymous (11th Century)
translated by Gustave Polack
Music: Latin melody (11th Century)
Harmony: for Celebration Hymnal
by Stephen Dean

© 1984 Mayhew-McCrimmon Ltd

1. Christ is arisen from the grave's dark prison.
   We now rejoice with gladness; Christ will end all sadness.
   Lord, have mercy.

2. All our hopes were ended had Jesus not ascended
   from the grave triumphantly. For this, Lord Christ, we worship Thee.
   Lord, have mercy.

3. Alleluia! Alleluia! Alleluia!
   We now rejoice with gladness; Christ will end all sadness.
   Lord, have mercy.

* As a pentitential rite for Eastertide, use the verses as tropes:

   in verses 1 & 3, have the people repeat the final **Lord, have mercy**
   in verse 2, use instead **Christ, have mercy** repeated by all.

426

Words and music:

N. & K. Donnelly

1. Christ is coming
   to set the captives free,
   He is coming
   to rescue you and me.

   Christ is coming from above
   bringing joy and bringing love.
   He is coming for you and me.

2. Christ has come
   to a stable cold and bare;
   He is coming
   to a world where no one cares.

3. Christ is coming,
   bringing light where darkness reigned;
   He is coming
   where we gather in his name.

4. Christ is coming
   to this altar in our Mass;
   He is coming
   to a new home in our hearts.

5. Christ is coming,
   the Father's only Son;
   He is coming
   – his spirit makes us one.

427 WESTMINSTER ABBEY (87.87.87)

1. Christ is made the sure foun- da- tion, Christ the head and corn- er stone, cho- sen of the Lord, and pre- cious, bind- ing all the Church in one, ho- ly Si- on's help for ev- er, and her con- fid- ence a- lone.

2. All that dedicated city,
   dearly loved of God on high,
   in exultant jubilation
   pours perpetual melody,
   God the One in Three adoring
   in glad hymns eternally,

3. To this temple where we call you
   come, O Lord of Hosts, today;
   with your wonted loving kindness
   hear your people as they pray,
   and your fullest benediction
   shed within its walls alway.

4. Here vouchsafe to all your servants
   what they ask of you to gain,
   what they gain of you forever
   with the blessed to retain,
   and hereafter in your glory
   evermore with you to reign.

5. Praise and honour to the Father,
   praise and honour to the Son,
   praise and honour to the Spirit,
   ever Three and ever One,
   consubstantial, co-eternal,
   while unending ages run.

Words: Anon., Latin 7th or 8th century, tr. John Mason Neale 1818-66 alt.
Music: Henry Purcell 1659-95, adapted by Ernest Hawkins 1802-68 from an anthem.

1. Christ is the world's light, he and none other;
   born in our darkness, he became our brother.
   If we have seen him, we have seen the Father:
   glory to God on high.

2. Christ is the world's peace, he and none other;
   no man can serve him and despise his brother.
   Who else unites us, one in God the Father?
   glory to God on high.

3. Christ is the world's life, he and none other,
   sold once for silver, murdered here, our brother
   he who redeems us, reigns with God the Father:
   glory to God on high.

4. Give God the glory, and none other;
   give God the glory, Spirit, Son and Father;
   give God the glory, God in man, my brother:
   glory to God on high.

Words: F. Pratt Green
Music: Paris Antiphoner (1681)

Words © Stainer & Bell Ltd

MOVILLE 76. 76 D

1. Christ is the world's redeemer,
   the lover of the pure,
   the fount of heavenly wisdom,
   our trust and hope secure,
   the armour of his soldiers,
   the lord of earth and sky,
   our health while we are living,
   our life when we shall die.

2. Christ has our host surrounded
   with clouds of martyrs bright
   who wave their palms in triumph
   and fire us for the fight.
   For Christ the cross ascended
   to save a world undone
   and suffering for the sinful
   our full redemption won.

3. Down in the realm of darkness
   he lay a captive bound,
   but at the hour appointed
   he rose, a victor crowned,
   and now, to heaven ascended,
   he sits upon the throne
   in glorious dominion,
   his Father's and his own.

Words: St Columba
translated by
Duncan McGregor
Music: Irish traditional

430

People

Christ our Lord has come to save his peo- ple! Al- le- lu-

ia! Al- le- lu- ia! Al- le- lu- ia!

VERSES

1. Baptised in Christ our Lord, re-born to new life in our Sa-viour and
2. O come then, bless the Lord, the Fa-ther of all, who is love with-out

Lord, al – le – lu – ia. For we are the peo – ple whom God made his
end, al – le – lu – ia. Be–fore he cre – a – ted the world with great

own through the blood of his own Son, our Lord Je – sus Christ.
pow'r we were cho–sen then in Christ, God made us his own.

3. Since time itself began
God loved us and planned to adopt us in Christ, alleluia!
He chose us to live in his glorious name,
as his children and his friends, a people redeemed.

4. Be joyful in the Lord,
rejoice and give thanks to the Father of all, alleluia!
For Christ is alive and we live now in him;
we are filled now with his life. Rejoice, praise his name!

5. With Christ we are made heirs
and called to belong to the fam'ly of God, alleluia!
Christ freed us from sin by his death on the cross,
and has raised us up to life, a life without end.

6. Give glory to our God, the Father of all;
to his Son, Jesus Christ, alleluia!
And praise to the Spirit, the gift of his love.
Let us sing out to the Lord for ever. Amen.

Words, based on Paul: Jean-Paul Lecot; Sister Lucia Fay; R. B. Kelly
Music: Paul Decha

Words and Music English language rights assigned 1984 to Kevin Mayhew Ltd.

431

Words and Music: Lucien Deiss © World Library Publications Inc.

ANTIPHON

Christ our Pasch has been slain, al-le-lu-ia! Sing with joy.

F Dm C F C G Dm Bb

Al-le-lu - ia, al-le-lu - ia, al-le-lu - ia! *Fine*

F Am Em Dm C G Dm Am Dm D

VERSES

1. Pasch of the New Law, the Spi-rit's ho-ly feast; O
2. Pasch of the New Law, O joy of all man-kind; the
3. Pasch of the New Law, the ban-quet hall is full of
4. Pasch of the New Law, our souls' im-mor-tal flame shines
5. Pasch of the New Law, our soul's im-mor-tal flame shines
6. Pasch of the New Law, O Christ who lives a - gain: the
7. Pasch of the New Law, we pray to you, O Lord: stretch
8. Pasch of the New Law, O Christ re - ceive our songs; to

Bb F C F Dm C G

1. Pasch of Christ the Lord, who for us has come to earth!
2. doors of life are wide, giv-ing life to us once more.
3. guests the Lord has called, that all men may share his feast.
4. robes of pur-est white for the mar-riage of the Lamb.
5. forth in splen-dor bright, ne-ver - more to cease its light.
6. pow'r of death you crushed, you have giv-en us your life.
7. forth your bless-ed hands on the peo - ple you have saved.
8. you be glo-ry, Lord, with all joy and praise. A - men!

C Am F Em Dm Bb Am

1. City of God, how broad and far
   outspread thy walls sublime!
   The true thy chartered freeman are,
   of every age and clime.

2. One holy Church, one army strong,
   one steadfast, high intent;
   one working band, one harvest-song,
   one King omnipotent.

3. How purely hath thy speech come down
   from man's primeval youth!
   How grandly hath thine empire grown,
   of freedom, love and truth!

4. How gleam thy watch-fires through the night
   with never-fainting ray!
   How rise thy towers, serene and bright, ·
   to meet the dawning day!

5. In vain the surge's angry shock,
   in vain the drifting sands:
   unharmed upon the eternal Rock
   the eternal City stands.

Words: Samuel Johnson (1822–82)
Music: Adapted from T. Haweis (1734–1820)
by S. Webbe (the younger) (c.1770–1843)

433 AVE VIRGO VIRGINUM (76.76.D)

1. Come, God's people, sing for joy,
   shout your songs of gladness;
   for the hope of Easter day
   overcomes our sadness.
   Come with all his people here,
   who with true affection,
   join again to celebrate
   Jesus' resurrection.

2. Years before, as Moses led
   Israel's sons and daughters
   from their bonds to Exodus
   through the Red Sea waters:
   so the living Lord of life
   speaks through our baptism
   of the new life that we share
   with him who is risen.

3. That first Easter he arose,
   his disciples greeting;
   Christians now throughout the world,
   still their Lord are meeting.
   Christ, who dies for all mankind,
   in his death brings healing;
   and his rising from the grave,
   God's power is revealing.

Words: St John Damascene d.c754
     freely paraphrased by Keith D.Pearson
Music: Leisentritt's Gesangbuch 1584

© 1976 Joint Board of Christian Education
     of Australia and New Zealand

Verse

E   B7

Refrain

E   B7

E   A   B7   E

1. Come, holy Lord, our faith renew;
   our little praise enough for you.

   We ask your mercy, Lord,
   who bear your sacred name;
   your healing touch
   the glorious blessing we can claim.

2. O Jesus, come, our hope on earth,
   from heaven you came to share our birth.

3. Come, Spirit blest, our love revive;
   our failing prayer is made alive.

Words and music: John Glynn

©1976 John Glynn

Harmony: for Celebration Hymnal
by John Rombaut

©1981 Mayhew-McCrimmon Ltd

435

Chorus

Come let us sing out our joy to the Lord! Hail the rock of sal-

va- tion, come in- to his presence to give him thanks,

sing- ing psalms of tri- umph.

Verses (cantor or choir)

1. In his hands are the depths of the earth, the moun- tain peaks be-
2. Bow down be- fore him in prayer, kneel be- fore the
3. Lis- ten to the voice of the Lord, do not grow stubborn nor
4. Praise the Fa- ther who made all things, praise the Son who

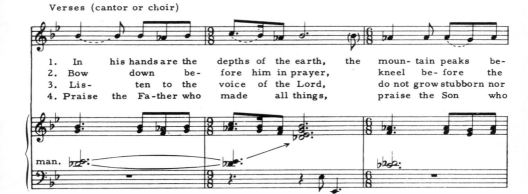

long to him. His is the sea, he cre- a- ted it,
Lord and a- dore. He is the Lord our shep-herd,
har-den your hearts. Put not your God to the test,
died for us. Praise the Spi- rit who glad-dens our hearts,

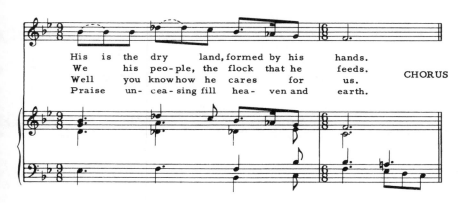

His is the dry land, formed by his hands.
We his peo-ple, the flock that he feeds. CHORUS
Well you know how he cares for us.
Praise un- cea-sing fill hea- ven and earth.

Words and Music: based on Psalm 94(95) © Stephen Dean

436

Refrain

Come, Lord Jesus, come Lord, come!   Come, Lord Jesus, come Lord

D   A7   D   D7   G   Gdim

come!   O – pen my eyes,   o – pen my mind,

Bm   Em   A7   F#m7   B7

peace   Fine   Verse

o–pen my heart to   and love.   1. Like rain falling on the   thirsty ground.

Em   A7   D   D   A7   D

spring- the
like grass -ing from bar-ren earth, like the sun ri-sing o - ver the land,

F#m   B7   Em   G   A7   F#m   Bm

her-alds new life and a new re - birth

A   E7   A   A7

2. So he comes bringing righteousness,
   bringing justice to all the land;
   so he comes as a man among men,
   Saviour and Lord of all mankind.

3. Wonder Counsellor and Prince of Peace,
   a man of such integrity!
   Come Lord Jesus, we plead to you,
   come and give us liberty.

Words: Scripture (Psalm 71 & Isaiah 9:6)
        adapted by Garfield Rochard
Music: Garfield Rochard

Harmony: for Celebration Hymnal
        by James O'Donnell

437

Verses

1. Come, O di- vine Mes- si- ah! The world in si- lence

waits the day when hope shall sing its tri- umph, and sad- ness flee a-

Chorus

way. Sweet Sa- viour, haste: come, come to earth, dis- pel the

night, and show thy face, and bid us hail the dawn of grace. Come,

O di-vine Mes- si- ah! The world in si-lence waits the day when

hope shall sing its tri- umph, and sad-ness flee a- way.

2. O Thou, whom nations sighed for,
   whom priests and prophets long foretold,
   wilt break the captive fetters,
   . redeem the long-lost fold.

3. Shalt come in peace and meekness,
   and lowly will thy cradle be:
   all clothed in human weakness
   shall we thy Godhead see.

Words: Abbe Pellegrin (1663-1745)
         tr. Sister Mary of St. Phillip, 1887
Music: 16th century French Carol,
         harmonised by Stephen Dean

438

Come, O Lord, to my heart today
and stay with me all the day.
Come, O Lord, to my heart today
and stay with me all the day.

1. Your flesh is food
   and your blood is drink,
   with these you give to me your life.

2. This is the bread
   come down from heaven
   which, if a man eats,
   he'll live for ever.

3. He who takes my flesh and blood
   lives in me and I in him.

4. When you give your self to us,
   you bind us to yourself
   and each other.

Words: based on John 6
         by Douglas Rowe
Music: Douglas Rowe
Harmony: for Celebration Hymnal
         by John Rombaut

439

CROSS OF JESUS (8.7.8.7)   First tune

STUTTGART (8.7.8.7)   Second tune

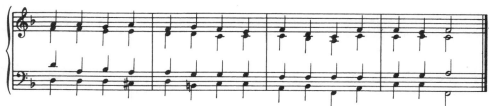

1. Come, thou long-expected Jesus,
   born to set thy people free;
   from our fears and sins release us;
   let us find our rest in thee.

2. Israel's strength and consolation,
   hope of all the earth thou art;
   dear Desire of every nation,
   joy of every longing heart.

3. Born thy people to deliver;
   born a Child and yet a King;
   born to reign in us for ever;
   now thy gracious kingdom bring.

4. By thy own eternal Spirit,
   rule in all our hearts alone:
   by thy all-sufficient merit,
   raise us to thy glorious throne.

Words: Charles Wesley (1707–88)
Music: 'Cross of Jesus' John Stainer (1840–1901), 'Stuttgart' C.F. Witt (1660–1716)

440

WACHET AUF   (898.D.664.88.)

1. Day and night the heav'ns are telling
    the glory which with us is dwelling,
    the works of God to us made known.
    Dawn and dusk are still with wonder.
    The wind cries out, the waters thunder,
    displaying his almighty power.
    Our God is great indeed.
    He knows our constant need, our creator.
    So with creation we proclaim
    his goodness as we praise his name.

2. Lord, we stand in awe before you,
    your people coming to adore you,
    so cleanse our hearts, renew our minds.
    See us now in shadows dwelling,
    and come like sun, the clouds dispelling,
    enlighten, heal us, Lord of love.
    Your Spirit in us prays.
    He teaches us your ways, as we listen.
    Touch once again with living flame
    your people gathered in your name.

Words: Pamela Stotter
Music: Melody by Philip Nicolai (1556-1608)
       adapted and harmonised by
       J.S.Bach (1685-1750)

441

three
Day by day, dear Lord of thee things I pray; to see thee more clear-ly, to

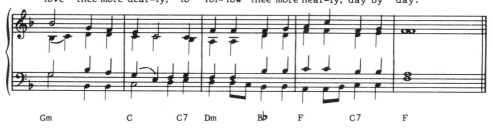

F   Gm   C   C7   Dm   G7   C   F   Dm

love thee more dear-ly, to fol-low thee more near-ly, day by day.

Gm   C   C7 Dm   B♭   F   C7   F

Words: Richard of Chichester
arranged by D. Austin

DUAN CHROI IOSA   (11 11 11 11)

1. Dear love of my heart, O heart of Christ, my Lord,
    what treasure you leave within my heart, O Guest!
    You come to my heart, O heart on fire with love,
    and leave me your heart: O how my heart is blest!

2. My heart cannot tell, O King of angel hosts,
    how great was that pain you bore upon the cross:
    so small is my heart, so deep your wounds of love,
    so precious the crown of those you save from loss!

3. Your death has restored your likeness in my heart,
    your cross is my shield, your loving heart my gain!
    How sad is my heart when I recall my sins!
    How could I have loved what gave your heart such pain?

4. O King of all bliss, all glory set aside,
    what heart could have known the pain within your breast?
    The wound in your side laid bare your burning love,
    and opened for all the heart where all find rest!

Words: based on the Irish of
        Tadhg Gaelach O Suilleabhain
        by James Quinn SJ
Music: Irish traditional

443 Unison

Refrain

Di – vi – ded our path-ways, and hea-vy our guilt; bur-den'd, un-

see –ing, we grope for the one way. Far from our home, O Fa-ther, we

call out, 'Heal us, for –give us: bring us to– ge–ther in Je–sus your Son!'

Fin e

Verse
Voice

1. Holy Father, keep those you have gi –ven me true to your Name,
2. Father, may they be one in us as you are in me and I am in you,
3. I have given them the glo–ry that you gave to me,
4. With me in them and you in me may they be so com-plete-ly u – nited,

1. so that they may all be one as we are one.
2. so that the world may come to be-lieve it was you who sent me.
3. that they may all be one as we are one.

4. that the world may know that it was you who sent me,

and that you love them as much as you love me.

Words: from John 17
      by Christopher Coelho OFM
Music: Christopher Coelho OFM

444

Chorus

Do not be a- fraid, for I have re- deemed you.

I have called you by your name; you are

mine. 1. When you walk through the wa-ters I'll be

fine

with you. You will nev- er sink be- neath the waves.

D.C.

2. When the fire is burning all around you,
   you will never be consumed by the flames,

3. When the fear of loneliness is looming,
   then remember I am at your side.

4. When you dwell in the exile of the stranger,
   remember you are precious in my eyes.

5. You are mine, O my child, I am your Father,
   and I love you with a perfect love.

Words (based on Isaiah 43:1–4) and Music: Gerard Markland

445

2. 'Do you really love me?'
Jesus said to Peter.
'Do you really love me?'
Jesus said again.
'Lord, you know I love you!'
Peter said with joy.
'Then feed my sheep,' he said,
'Peter, feed my sheep.' ▷ ▷ ▷

Words & Music: Carey Landry

446 (88.88)

If another tune is desired, consult the metrical index.

1. Each morning with its new born light
   proclaims the Lord of life is great!
   His faithfulness will have no end;
   to him our songs of praise ascend.

2. The gift of light that fills the sky
   helps us to see and choose our way;
   then let us order our affairs
   in praise of him who for us cares.

3. Lord, let our eyes, the body's light,
   be drawn to what is good and right
   and to yourself, the source of life,
   our hope in fear, our peace in strife.

4. You, Lord of all creation, are
   as brilliant as the morning star;
   light in our hearts your holy flame
   and make us fit to bear your name.

5. Dispel the darkness from our days
   and free us from all bitterness,
   from haughty mind and blinded sight,
   and lead us forward day and night.

6. To walk as in the light of day,
   be steadfast always, come what may,
   we turn in faith to you, our Friend,
   and pray: sustain us to the end.

Words: Johannes Zwick (1496–1570)
translated by Fred Kaan
Music: Johann Walter (1541)

© 1972 Fred Kaan

Refrain *Calmly*

Faith in God can move the moun-tains; trust in him can calm the sea.

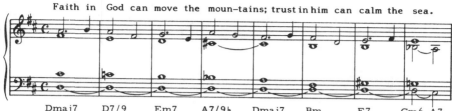

Dmaj7 D7/9 Em7 A7/9♭ Dmaj7 Bm E7 Gm6 A7

He's my for-tress, he's my strong-hold; he's the rock who res-cues me.

Dmaj7 D7/9 Em7 A7 D Am7 B7 Gm6 A7 D

Verse
Lord, you are my re — fuge; ne — ver let me be a - shamed.

G6 F♯7 Bm G Gm7 D

and
In your jus - tice res - cue me; turn to me hear my prayer.

Gm7 C7 Fmaj7 A E7 Gm6 A7

2. You are my salvation:
from oppression set me free.
Ever since my childhood
you have been my only hope.

3. Bitter troubles burden me,
but you fill me with new life.
From the grave you raise me up,
so my tongue will sing your praise.

Words paraphrased from Scripture
by Aniceto Nazareth
Music: Aniceto Nazareth

448

*The metre of this hymn is irregular. The slurs in the melody
apply to verse 1 only.*

1. Fashion me a people,
   a people set apart;
   that I may be your God,
   and you will give me your heart.

2. Come together in community,
   a sign of my love here on earth,
   to share the life of Nazareth,
   and incarnate the myst'ry of my birth.

3. Be a fam'ly, humble and forgiving,
   who listen to my voice,
   who call upon my mercy,
   and at my coming rejoice.

4. Fashion me a people,
   a people set apart;
   that I may be your God,
   and I will give you my heart.

Words and music: Carol McCollin

Harmony: for Celebration Hymnal
          by Eric Welch

© 1981 Mayhew—McCrimmon Ltd

1. Fa-ther, hear the prayer we off-er: not for ease that prayer shall be,

but for strength that we may ev- er live our lives cour- a-geous-ly.

2. Not for ever in green pastures
   do we ask our way to be;
   but the steep and rugged pathway
   may we tread rejoicingly.

3. Not for ever by still waters
   would we idly rest and stay;
   but would smite the living foundations
   from the rocks along the way.

4. Be our strength in hours of weakness,
   in our wanderings be our guide;
   through endeavour, failure, danger,
   Father, be there at our side.

Words: Love Maria Willis (1824-1908) and others
Music: English traditional melody, collected, adapted
    and arranged by Ralph Vaughan Williams (1872-1958)

© Oxford University Press

450a

Two sample accompaniments (repeat over and over again, or improvise ad lib.) when verses are sung as a round:-

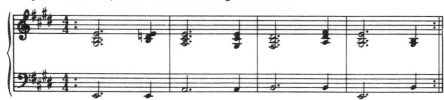

Accompaniment when verses are sung in unison:-

1. Fa- ther, I   place in- to your   hands the things that   I can't do;

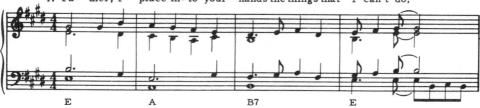

E   A   B7   E

Fa- ther I   place in- to your   hands the times that I've been through;

E   A   B7   E

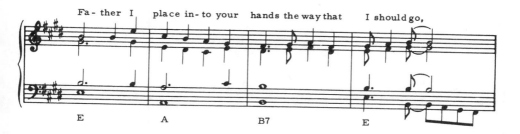

Fa - ther I place in- to your hands the way that I should go,

For I know I al-ways can trust you.

2. Father, I place into your hands my friends and family;
   Father, I place into your hands the things that trouble me;
   Father, I place into your hands the person I should be,
   for I know I always can trust you.

3. Father, we love to seek your face, we love to hear your voice;
   Father, we love to sing your praise, and in your name rejoice;
   Father, we love to walk with you and in your presence rest,
   for we know we always can trust you.

4. Father, I want to be with you and do the things you do;
   Father, I want to speak the words that you are speaking too;
   Father, I want to love the ones that you will draw to you,
   for I know that I am one with you.

Words: J. Hewer
Music: Ernest Sands

Words © 1975 J. Hewer and Thankyou Music, Eastbourne.
Melody © 1981 Ernest Sands. Arrangements © 1984 Magnificat Music, London.

450b

1. Fa-ther, I place in — to your hands the things I can-not do,

F(E)   C(B7)

Fa-ther, I place in — to your hands the times that I've been through.

F(E)

Fa-ther, I place in — to your hands the way that I should go, for I

F7(E7)   Bb6(A6)   Bbm(Am)

know I al - ways can trust you. -----------

F(E)   C(B7)   F(C)

Verses 2-4 as 450a, previous page.

Words and Music: J. Hewer
© *1975, J. Hewer and Thankyou Music, Eastbourne*

HALAD (55.55.55.54)

1. Father in heaven,
   grant to your children
   mercy and blessing,
   songs never ceasing,
   love to unite us,
   grace to redeem us,
   Father in heaven,
   Father our God.

2. Jesus, Redeemer,
   may we remember
   your gracious Passion,
   your resurrection.
   Worship we bring you,
   praise we shall sing you
   Jesus, Redeemer,
   Jesus our God.

3. Spirit descending,
   whose is the blessing –
   strength for the weary,
   help for the needy,
   sealed in our sonship
   yours be our worship –
   Spirit unending,
   Spirit adored.

Words: D.T. Niles
Music: Philippines traditional
       arranged by Elena G. Maquiso
       harmony by Cantate Domino

452 TRINITY SONG

Effective when men's voices sing one line, and women's the other.

Fa- ther, in my life I see, you are

GROUP 2: Fa-ther, in my life I see,

G   C   Am   D

God, who walks with me. You hold my life in your

you are God, who walks with me.

G   Em

hands: close be- side you I will stand.

You hold my life in your hands: close be-

Am   D   G

I give all my life to you:

side you I will stand.   I give all my life to

Em   Am

Last time   fine   Interlude between verses

help me, Fa - ther, to be true.

you.   true.

fine

D   C   G   Am   D7

2. Jesus, in my life I see...

3. Spirit, in my life I see...

Words and Music: Frank Anderson, M.S.C.
© Chevalier Press, Australia

453 ABBOTS LEIGH (87.87.D)

1. Fa- ther, Lord of all cre- a- tion, ground of

be- ing, life and love; height and depth be-

yond de- scription, on- ly life in you can

prove: you are mor- tal life's de- pen- dence: thought, speech,

sight   are   ours   by   grace;   yours   is   ev- ery   hour's   ex-

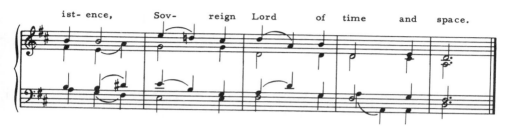

ist- ence,   Sov-   reign   Lord   of   time   and   space.

2. Jesus Christ, the man for others,
   we, your people, make our prayer:
   give us grace to love as brothers
   all whose burdens we can share.
   Where your name binds us together
   you, Lord Christ, will surely be;
   where no selfishness can sever
   there your love may all men see.

3. Holy Spirit, rushing, burning
   wind and flame of Pentecost,
   fire our hearts afresh with yearning
   to regain what we have lost.
   May your love unite our action,
   nevermore to speak alone:
   God, in us abolish faction,
   God, through us your love make known.

Words: Stewart Cross
Music: Cyril Taylor

Alternative words:

1. Glorious things of you are spoken,
   Sion, city of our God:
   he whose word cannot be broken
   formed you for his own abode.
   On the Rock of Ages founded,
   what can shake your sure repose?
   With salvation's walls surrounded,
   you may smile at all your foes.

2. See, the streams of living waters,
   springing from eternal love,
   well supply your sons and daughters
   and all fear of want remove:
   who can faint while such a river
   ever flows their thirst to assuage -
   grace, which like the Lord the giver
   never fails from age to age?

3. Blest inhabitants of Sion,
   washed in their Redeemer's blood;
   Jesus, whom their souls rely on,
   makes them Kings and priests to God.
   'Tis his love his people raises
   over self to reign as kings,
   and as priests, his solemn praises
   each for a thank-offering brings.

4. Saviour, since of Sion's city
   I, through grace, a member am,
   let the world deride or pity,
   I will glory in your name:
   fading is the worldling's pleasure,
   all his boasted pomp and show;
   solid joys and lasting treasure
   none but Sion's children know.

Words: John Newton (1725-1807)

454 SONG 5 (88.88)

2. Almighty Son, incarnate Word,
   our prophet, priest, Redeemer, Lord,
   before thy throne we sinners bend,
   to us thy saving grace extend.

3. Eternal Spirit, by whose breath
   the soul is raised from sin and death,
   before thy throne we sinners bend,
   to us thy quickening power extend.

4. Thrice Holy! Father, Spirit, Son;
   Mysterious Godhead, Three in One,
   before thy throne we sinners bend,
   grace, pardon, life to us extend.

Words: E. Cooper 1770-1833
Music: Melody and bass by O. Gibbons 1583-1625
    (rhythm slightly altered)

455

1. Father, we praise you, now the night is over;
   active and watchful stand we all before you;
   singing, we offer pray'r and meditation:
   thus we adore you.

2. Monarch of all things, fit us for your kingdom;
   banish our weakness, health and wholeness sending;
   bring us to heaven, where your saints united
   joy without ending.

3. All holy Father, Son, and equal Spirit,
   Trinity blessed, send us your salvation;
   yours is the glory, gleaming and resounding
   through all creation.

Words: Gregory the Great (540-604)
        translated by Percy Dearmer (1867-1936)
Music: La Feillee's Methode du Plain Chant (1808)
        harmonised by David Evans

© Oxford University Press

456

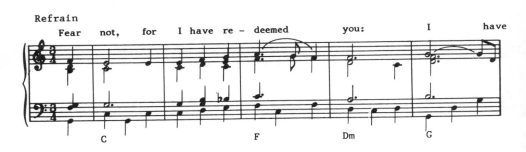

Refrain

Fear not, for I have re - deemed you: I have

C   F   Dm   G

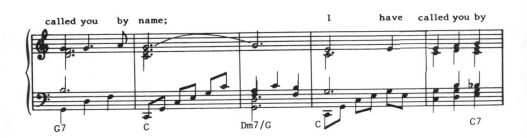

called you by name; I have called you by

G7   C   Dm7/G   C   C7

name; you are mine.

F   Dm   G   G7   C

Where verse follows | Last time | Verse

C7   C   (C7)   G   C   Am

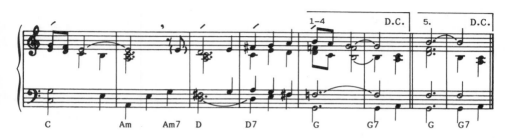

1. When you páss through the wáters
I will bé with you;
and through rívers,
they will nót overwhélm you.
When you wálk through the fíre
you will nót be burned,
the flámes shall nót consúme you.

2. Becáuse you are précious,
and I lóve you;
yóu whom I fórmed
for my glóry;
yóu whom I cálled
by my náme,
I will gáther togéther.

3. Yóu are my wítness;
I have chósen you
thát you may knów
and belíeve me.
Yóu are my sérvants
for the wórld to see
I am the Lórd, I'm amóng you.

4. It's tíme now to láy aside
the fórmer things;
a néw day has dáwned,
do you sée it?
I'm máking a wáy
in the wílderness
and rívers to flów in the désert.

5. The rívers that flów
in the désert
give drínk
to my chosen péople;
to quénch their thírst
and to stréngthen them
that théy might show fórth my práise.

Words: based on Isaiah 43
by Jodi Page
Music: Jodi Page

© 1975 Celebration Services (International)

The metre of the verses is irregular. However, with practice
it will be found easy to fit in the syllables between the accents.
In verses 2 & 3 some upbeats (shown in brackets in the music)
are omitted.

457

Fear not, re- joice and be glad, the

Em

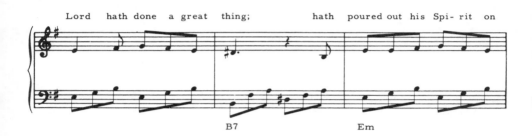

Lord hath done a great thing; hath poured out his Spi- rit on

B7   Em

all man-kind, on those who con- fess his name.   1. The

fine

Am   Em   B7   Em

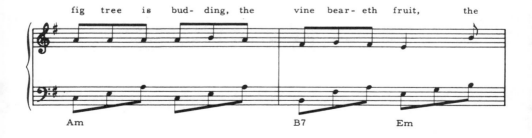

fig tree is bud- ding, the vine bear- eth fruit, the

Am   B7   Em

wheat-fields are gol-den with grain.   Thrust in the sick-le, the

Am   E   Am

har-vest is ripe, the Lord has giv-en us rain.

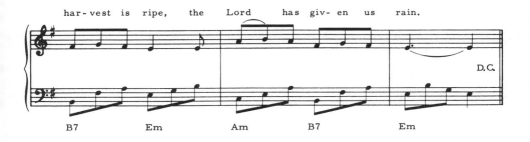

D.C.

B7   Em   Am   B7   Em

2. Ye shall eat in plenty and be satisfied,
   the mountains will drip with sweet wine.
   My children shall drink of the fountain of life,
   my children will know they are mine.

3. My people shall know that I am the Lord,
   their shame I have taken away.
   My Spirit will lead them together again,
   my Spirit will show them the way.

4. My children shall dwell in a body of love,
   a light to the world they will be.
   Life shall come forth from the Father above,
   my body will set mankind free.

Words and Music: Priscilla Wright Porter

© 1971, 1975 Celebration Services (International) Ltd.

458

1. "Feed my lambs, my son, feed my sheep;
   if you love me, do not sleep.
   In the fields, my son, work and weep;
   feed my lambs, my son, feed my sheep."

2. To the servant girl first he lied:
   "You were with him!" this she cried.
   But the Master he denied;
   on the fol'wing day, Jesus died.

3. Someone questioned him quietly,
   "Aren't you Peter of Galilee?
   I can tell you by your speech, you see."
   Peter swore and said, "It's not me!"

4. Peter heard the cock when it crew;
   as he left, he wept – and he knew!
   Ev'ry one of us is guilty too;
   yet Christ died for us, me and you.

5. "Feed my lambs, my son, feed my sheep;
   if you love me, do not sleep.
   In the fields, my son, work and weep;
   feed my lambs, my son, feed my sheep."

Words: Charles A. Buffham (altered)
Music: Charles A. Buffham

1969 Singspiration, Inc.

Harmony: for Celebration Hymnal
         by Frances M. & Robert B. Kelly

© 1981 Mayhew-McCrimmon Ltd

The tune Grosser Gott (No.212) will also fit this hymn.

1. Firm is our faith in one true God,
   loving Father and King supreme,
   mighty creator, Lord of all,
   visible world and world unseen.

2. And we believe in God's own Son,
   one with him from eternal dawn,
   who by the Spirit was conceived,
   and of his Virgin Mother born.

3. Man he was made and man he lived,
   man he suffered in cruel strife,
   when on the Cross he fought with death,
   conquered and rose to deathless life.

4. This is our faith in the Spirit too:
   Lord and giver of life is he,
   one with the Father and the Son,
   spirit of love and unity.

5. Faith we profess in one true Church,
   sin forgiven and grace restored,
   hope for the vict'ry over death,
   life without end in Christ the Lord.

Words: Denis E. Hurley
Music: Moira G. Kearney

© Archdiocese of Durban, South Africa

460

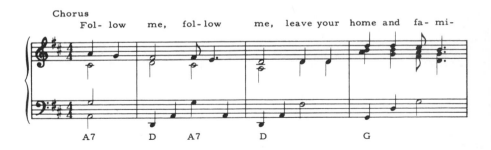

Fol- low me, fol- low me, leave your home and fa- mi-

A7   D   A7   D   G

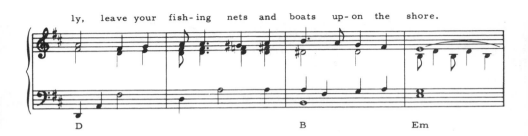

ly, leave your fish- ing nets and boats up- on the shore.

D   B   Em

Leave the seed that you have sown, leave the crops that you've

A7   D   A7   D   G

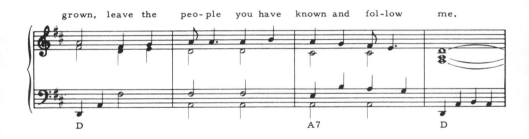

grown, leave the peo- ple you have known and fol- low me.

D   A7   D

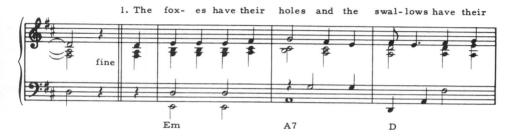

1. The fox-es have their holes and the swal-lows have their

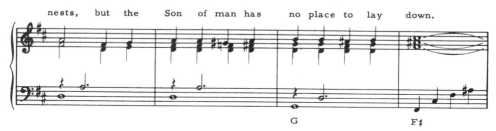

nests, but the Son of man has no place to lay down.

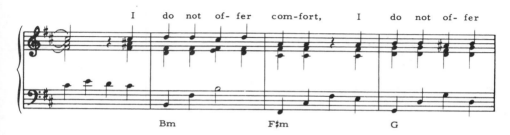

I do not of-fer com-fort, I do not of-fer

wealth, but in me will all hap-pi-ness be found.

2. If you would follow me,
   you must leave old ways behind.
   You must take my cross
   and follow on my path.
   You may be far from loved ones,
   you may be far from home,
   but my Father will welcome you at last.

3. Although I go away
   you will never be alone,
   for the Spirit will be
   there to comfort you.
   Though all of you may scatter,
   each follow his own path,
   still the Spirit of love will lead you home.

Words: Michael Cockett
Music: Sister Madeleine, F.C.J.

© 1978 Kevin Mayhew Ltd.

461 EAST ACKLAM (84.84.888.4)

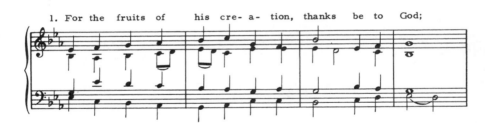

1. For the fruits of his cre-a-tion, thanks be to God;

for his gifts to ev-'ry na-tion, thanks be to God;

for the ploughing, sow-ing, reaping, si-lent growth while men are sleeping,

fu-ture needs in earth's safe keep-ing, thanks be to God.

2. In the just reward of labour,
   God's will is done;
   in the help we give our neighbour,
   God's will is done;
   in our world-wide task of caring
   for the hungry and despairing,
   in the harvests men are sharing,
   God's will is done.

3. For the harvests of his Spirit,
   thanks be to God;
   for the good all men inherit,
   thanks be to God;
   for the wonders that astound us,
   for the truths that still confound us,
   most of all, that love has found us,
   thanks be to God.

Words: F. Pratt Green
Music: Francis Jackson

Words © Stainer & Bell Ltd. Music © Francis Jackson.

1. For the healing of the nations,
   Lord, we pray with one accord;
   for a just and equal sharing
   of the things that earth affords.
   To a life of love in action
   help us rise and pledge our word.

2. Lead us, father, into freedom,
   from despair your world release;
   that redeemed from war and hatred,
   men may come and go in peace.
   Show us how through care and goodness
   fear will die and hope increase.

3. All that kills abundant living,
   let it from the earth be banned;
   pride of status, race or schooling,
   dogmas keeping man from man.
   In our common quest for justice
   may we hallow life's brief span.

4. You, creator-God, have written
   your great name on all mankind;
   for our growing in your likeness
   bring the life of Christ to mind;
   that by our response and service
   earth its destiny may find.

Words: Fred Kaan
Music: French traditional carol

Words © 1968 Galliard Ltd

463

Chorus

For to those who love God, who are called in his plan, ev'-ry- thing works out for good.

And God him- self chose them to bear the like- ness of his Son, that he might be the first of ma- ny, ma- ny broth-ers.

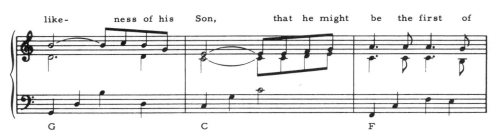

C

Am

Dm

G

C

Am

F

Dm

Am

Dm

G

C

F

Dm

G7

G7

1-3

Last time

broth-

ers.   1. Who is   a-   ble to con-

fine

C   C

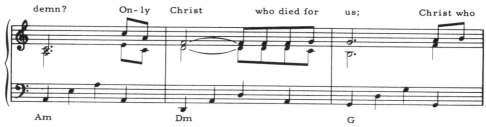

demn?   On-ly Christ   who died for   us;   Christ who

Am   Dm   G

rose   for   us;   Christ who prays   for   us.

1. 2.

D.C.

Am   Dm   F   G

3. 4.

D.C.

G

2. In the face of all this   3. What can separate us
   what is there left to say?   from the love of Christ?
   For if God is with us,   Neither trouble, nor pain,
   who can be against us?   nor persecution.

4. What can separate us
   from the love of Christ?
   Not the past, the present,
   nor the future.

Words (based on Romans 8:28-38) and Music: Enrico Garzilli

©1970 Rev. Enrico Garzilli

464

1. For un-to us a child is born, un-to

us a son is giv-en; and the gov-ern-ment shall

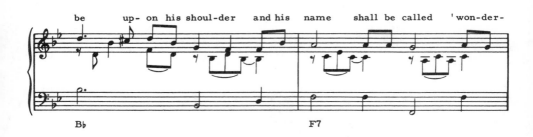

be up-on his shoul-der and his name shall be called 'won-der-

ful - coun-sel-lor', 'the migh-ty God', 'the

Words: Based on Isaiah 9: 6
Music: Unknown, arranged by Roger Humphrey

465

Introduction

Em   Em7   C   Am7

Refrain
Free- ly,
Flowing
D   Em   B7   Em   Bm

I give to you the gift of a child, my
Am   C   Am7   D

own, in hope that you will re-
Em   B   Em   Bm   Am

ceive the life that he gives for your own.
C   Am7   D   G   G/C

(To verse) (Last time bar)
Fine

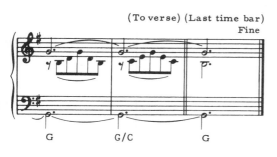

G   G/C   G

Verses

1. Call him E- man- uel, for your God is

G   C   D   Em   C

with you this day. He'll be by your side

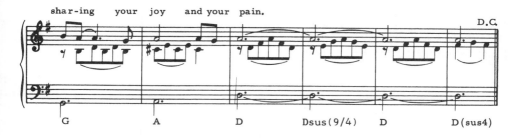

G   D   Em   C

shar-ing your joy and your pain.

D.C.

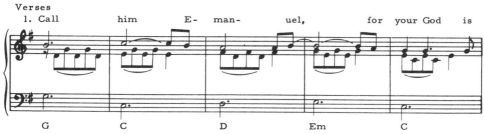

G   A   D   Dsus(9/4)   D   D(sus4)

2. Call him Je- sus, for Yah- weh

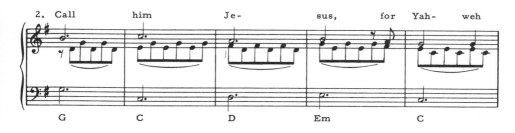

G   C   D   Em   C

saves his own. For he is the shep-herd who will
guide his flock safe-ly home.

D.C.

3. Call him Lamb of God for he has
died for your sins and all will be saved and
tru- ly be- long to him.

D.C.

Words and Music: J.Garrity, arranged by Roger Humphrey
© 1984 United Kingdom Rights, Mayhew-McCrimmon Ltd

Dm   Gm   Dm   Gm6   A7   Dm   Gm   Dm

Gm   A   Dm   D7   Gm   C7

F   Gm6   Dm   Gm   A7   Dm   Dm

1. From the depths of sin and sadness
   I have called unto the Lord;
   be not deaf to my poor pleading,
   in your mercy, hear my voice.
   Be not deaf to my poor pleading,
   in your mercy, hear my voice.

2. If you, Lord, record our sinning
   who could then before you stand?
   But with you there is forgiveness;
   you shall ever be revered.
   But with you there is forgiveness;
   you shall ever be revered.

3. For the Lord my heart is waiting,
   for his word I hope and wait.
   More than watchmen wait for sunrise
   I am waiting for the Lord.
   More than watchmen wait for sunrise
   I am waiting for the Lord.

4. Hope, O people, in your Saviour,
   he will save you from your sin.
   Jesus from his cross is praying,
   "Father, forgive them, they know not what they do."
   Jesus from his cross is praying,
   "Father, forgive them, they know not what they do."

Words: based on Psalm 129/130
      by Willard F. Jabusch
Music: Russian traditional
      arranged by Willard F. Jabusch

©1966 Willard F. Jabusch

Harmony © 1984 Mayhew-McCrimmon Ltd

467

Gather Christians, let's now celebrate;
gather Christians, the Lord we now await;
gather Christians, behold he comes;
rejoice and sing, for the Lord is King!

1   *To God the Father, let's give him praise;
to God the Father, our voice we raise;
to God the Father, who reigns above;
praise the Lord for his mercy and his love.

2. As we stand here before our God,
with Christ Jesus, our saving Lord,
we'll break his word now, and break the bread,
as we proclaim: he's risen from the dead!

3. Let us all now, as one community,
praise and honour the Trinity.
Let us all now with one accord
sing out our praise to the living Lord!

An extra note is added at the beginning of this line.

Words and music: Garfield Rochard
Harmony for Celebration Hymnal
by Eric Welch

© *1981 Mayhew McCrimmon Ltd*

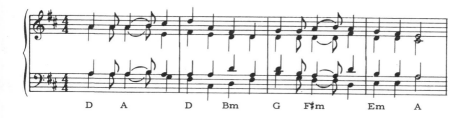

D   A   D   Bm   G   F♯m   Em   A

D   D7   G   B   Em   A   D   F♯

Bm   F♯m   B   Em   E7   A   A7   D   A7   D

1. Gathered here from many churches,*
   one in worship and intent,
   let us for the days that face us
   all our hopes to God present,
   that our life and work may be
   symbols of our unity.

2. May the spring of all our actions
   be, O Lord, your love for man;
   may your word be seen and spoken
   and your will be clearly done.
   Help us, who your image bear,
   for the good of each to care.

   * or Gathered here from many nations,

3. Give us grace to match our calling,
   faith to overcome the past;
   show us how to meet the future,
   planning boldly, acting fast.
   Let the servant-mind of Christ
   in our life be manifest.

4. Now ourselves anew committing
   to each other and to you,
   Lord, we ask that you will train us
   for the truth we have to do;
   that the world may soon become
   your great city of shalom.

NOTE: The keyboard harmonisation and the guitar
chords should **not** be used together.

Words: Fred Kaan
Music: Doreen Potter

© 1972 Galliard Ltd

469

Gifts of bread and wine, gifts we've of - fered,

D   Em   A   G   D

fruits of la - bour, fruits of love;

Em   A   G   D

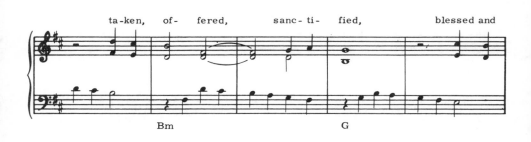

ta - ken, of - fered, sanc - ti - fied, blessed and

Bm   G

bro - ken; words of one who died: 'Take my

A   G   D

bo-   dy;   take   my   sav- ing blood.'   Gifts of

Em   A   G   D

bread   and wine: Christ our   Lord.

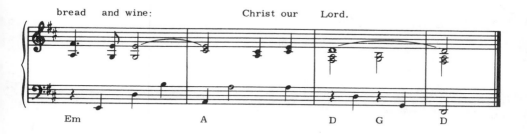

Em   A   D   G   D

2. Christ our Saviour, living presence here,
   as he promised while on earth:
   'I am with you for all time,
   I am with you in this bread and wine.
   Take my body, take my saving blood.'
   Gifts of bread and wine: Christ our Lord.

3. Through the Father, with the Spirit,
   one in union with the Son,
   for God's people, joined in prayer
   faith is strengthened by the food we share.
   'Take my body, take my saving blood.'
   Gifts of bread and wine: Christ our Lord.

Words and Music: Christine McCann

© 1978 Kevin Mayhew Ltd.

470

Note: Guitar chords should not be played with the organ accompaniment.

1. Give praise to the Lord, all you men, al-le-lu — ia! O praise the
name of the Lord, al-le-lu — ia! Blessed be the name of the Lord, al-le-lu —
ia, al-le-lu-ia! 2. Now and ev-er-more, al-le-lu — ia! From dawn to
close of the day, al-le-lu — ia! Blessed be the name of the

Lord, al-le-lu — ia, al-le-lu-ia! 3. On high a-bove the earth is the

Dm   F   Gm Bb   C Dm   C   F

Lord, al-le-lu — ia! His glo-ry a-bove the sky al-le-lu — ia!

Dm   A   A7   Dm   G   C   F   A

There is none like the Lord our God, al-le-lu — ia, al-le-lu-ia! 4. En-

A7   Dm   F   Dm   F   Gm Bb   C   Dm

throned in heaven on high, al-le-lu — ia! He views the earth and the sky, al-le-

F   Dm   A   A7   Dm   G   C

lu — ia! To those in need he gives his help, al-le-lu — ia,

F   A   A7   Dm   F   Dm   F   Gm

7. Let us sing to the Lord, al-le-lu — ia! Sing-ing glo-ry and praise al-le-

lu — ia! Both now and ev-er-more, Amen, al-le-lu — ia, al-le-lu — ia!

Words (based on Psalm 113) and Music: Lucien Deiss

471

Em Bm Em Am Em D G Bm G D Bm Em Am Em

1. Give us the will to listen to the message you impart:
    we thank you, Lord, for showing us your heart!

2. Give us the will to persevere though meaning disappears:
    we thank you, Lord, for calming all our fears.

3. Give us the will to work on at what we may like the least:
    we thank you, Lord, for ev'ry bird and beast.

4. Give us the will to work and serve where we are needed most:
    we thank you, Lord, for staying with us close.

5. Give us the will to seek you in the quiet and the calm:
    we thank you, Lord, for keeping us from harm.

6. Give us the will to see you as our God, as man, as friend:
    we thank you, Lord, for your love has no end.

Words: Kurt Rommel
          translated by Eileen M. Burzynska
Music: Kurt Rommel

Original German © Burckhardhaus-Verlag, Geilnhausen
English arrangement ©1980 Mayhew-McCrimmon Ltd

Harmony: for Celebration Hymnal
          by Eric Welch

©1981 Mayhew-McCrimmon Ltd

472

Glorious things of you are spoken

*The words and accompanying tune to this hymn
will be found with No.453.*

473

Spirited, very deliberate (♩ = 162)

Ped.

G   D   Em   Bm   C

Em   D   D9/C   G/B   D/A

ANTIPHON

Glo- ry and praise to our God, who a- lone gives

G   D   Em   G

light to our days. Man- y are the blessings he

D   Am   C   G

bears   to   those   who   trust   in   his   ways.   (Verses)

Bm   Ped.   C   D   G

Verses 1 - 3

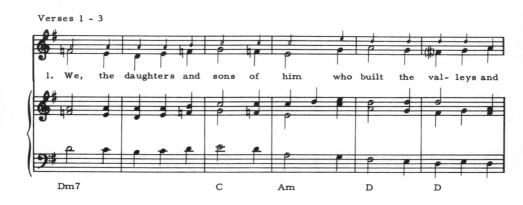

1. We,   the   daughters   and   sons   of   him   who   built   the   val- leys and

Dm7   C   Am   D   D

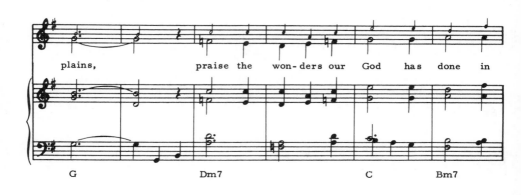

plains,   praise   the   won- ders   our   God   has   done   in

G   Dm7   C   Bm7

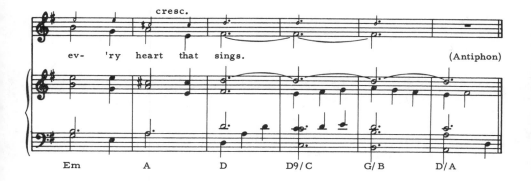

ev- 'ry heart that sings.　　　　　　　　(Antiphon)

Em　　A　　D　　D9/C　　G/B　　D/A

2. In his wisdom he strengthens us,
   like gold that's tested in fire.
   Though the power of sin prevails,
   our God is there to save.

Antiphon

3. Ev'ry moment of ev'ry day
   our God is waiting to save,
   always ready to seek the lost,
   to answer those who pray.

Antiphon

(Verse 4 – see over)

Verse 4

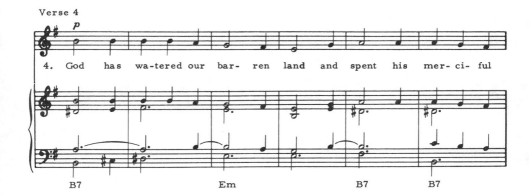

4. God has wa-tered our bar- ren land and spent his mer- ci- ful

B7   Em   B7   B7

. rain.   Now   the riv- ers of life   run full   for

Em   C   G   Em

an- y- one to   drink.   (Antiphon)

Am   D   D9/C G/B   D/A

Words (based on Psalms 65 & 66) and Music: Dan Schutte, S.J.,
Arr. by Sr.Theophane Hytrek, O.S.F.

**Glory to God! Peace to all men,
joy to earth comes from heaven.**

1. For all your wonders, O Lord God,
    your people come to thank you.
    Our gracious friend, we bless your name,
    for your Kingdom which comes!
    To you we bring our praises
    through the love of the Son and of the Spirit.

2. The world's redeemer, Jesus Christ,
    receive the pray'r we bring you.
    O Lamb of God, you conquered death;
    now have mercy on us.
    Most holy Jesus, Son of God:
    living Lord of all worlds, our Lord God!

Words: AELF, translated by Erik Routley
Music: Jacques Berthier

Words ©1972 Erik Routley
Music ©SEFIM

475 MOSCOW (664.6664)

1. God, at creation's dawn,
   over a world unborn,
   your Spirit soared.
   By word and water deign
   that this same Spirit reign
   in those now born again,
   through Christ our Lord.

2. We, who in Adam fell,
   are, as the Scriptures tell,
   saved and restored.
   For, when these rites are done,
   dying we are made one,
   rising we overcome,
   with Christ our Lord.

3. Hear us, your Church, rejoice,
   singing with grateful voice,
   Father adored;
   telling our faith anew,
   greeting with welcome true
   children new born to you,
   in Christ our Lord.

Words: Denis E. Hurley

© Archdiocese of Durban, South Africa

Music: Felice de Giardini (1716–96), adapted

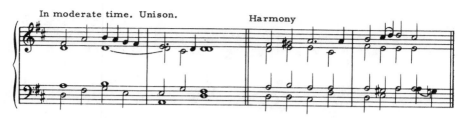

1. God be with you till we meet again;
    by his counsels guide, uphold you,
    with his sheep securely fold you:
    God be with you till we meet again.

2. God be with you till we meet again;
    'neath his wings protecting hide you,
    daily manna still provide you:
    God be with you till we meet again.

3. God be with you till we meet again;
    when life's perils thick confound you,
    put his arm unfailing round you:
    God be with you till we meet again.

4. God be with you till we meet again;
    keep love's banner floating o'er you,
    smite death's threatening wave before you:
    God be with you till we meet again.

Words: J.E. Rankin
Music: R. Vaughan Williams

477

Verse

God for-gave my sin in Je - sus' name; I've been born a -

D Bm Em A7 Em

- gain in Je - sus name; and in Je - sus' name I come to you to

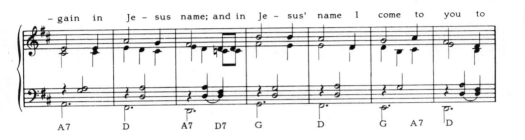

A7 D A7 D7 G D G A7 D

share his love as he told me to. He said: "Free - ly, free - ly,

Refrain

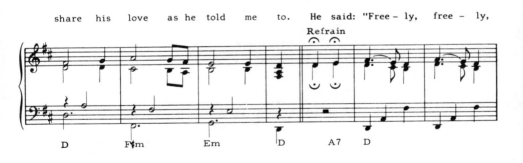

D F#m Em D A7 D

you have re - ceived; free - ly, free - ly, give. Go in my

Em A7 A7 D

name, and be—cause you be – lieve,   othe—rs will know that I   live."

Em   A7   A7   D

2. All pow'r is giv'n in Jesus' name,
   in earth and heav'n in Jesus' name;
   and in Jesus' name I come to you
   to share his pow'r as he told me to.

3. God gives us life in Jesus' name,
   he lives in us in Jesus' name;
   and in Jesus' name I come to you
   to share his peace as he told me to.

Words and Music: Carol Owens

© 1972 Lexicon Music, Inc.

478

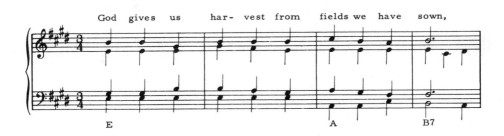

God gives us har- vest from fields we have sown,

E   A   B7

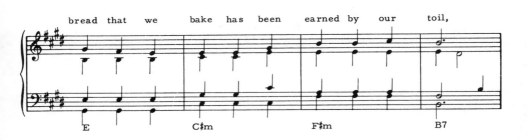

bread that we bake has been earned by our toil,

E   C♯m   F♯m   B7

bread of our sad- ness we bring to the Lord.

E   A   E   B7   E

LEADER

Praise to the Lord of the har- vest.

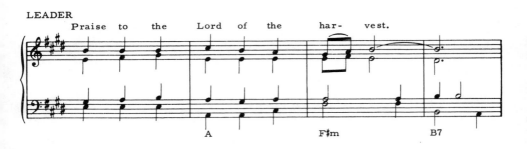

A   F♯m   B7

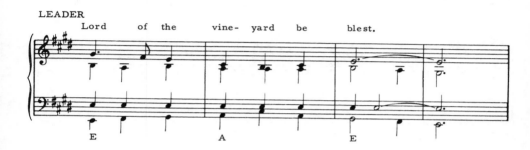

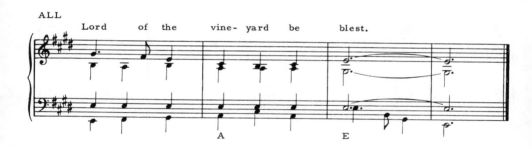

2. God has made fruitful the vines we have grown,
   wine that we make has been pressed for our joy,
   wine of our gladness we bring to the Lord.
   Praise to the Lord of the harvest.
   Praise to the Lord of the harvest.
   Lord of the vineyard be blest.
   Lord of the vineyard be blest.

Words: Patrick Lee
Music: Michael Coy

479

Chorus

God has glad – dened my heart with joy, al – le – lu – ia! He has vest – ed me with ho – li – ness, al – le – lu – ia!

Verse 1 (Soloist)

Sing my soul of the glo – ry of the Lord; with God's Spi – rit I'm full to ov – er flow – ing!

Verse 2 (Choir, Ad.Lib.)

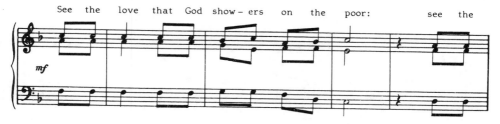

See the love that God show-ers on the poor: see the

Lord ov-er-shad-ow those who fear him.

Alternate verses as above

3. All the world will join in this song of praise,
   for through me they now know the Lord is with them.

4. To fulfill what he promised from of old
   God has chosen me! Bless his name for ever.

5. Day by day, year by year, God's love is sure;
   those who listen and keep his word will know it.

6. See the pow'r of the Lord destroy the strong!
   Those who think themselves strong, the Lord will humble.

7. Empty pride, self conceit, the Lord ignores;
   but he raises the poor who call upon him.

8. No more thirst, no more hunger with the Lord;
   unsurpassed in his goodness to his people.

9. See the care that the Lord shows to us all.
   Day by day, year by year, God's love's unending.

10. Praise the Father, the Son, the Spirit, praise!
    May the glory of God be sung for ever.

Words; based on Luke 1:46–55: Jean-Paul Lecot; W.R.Lawrence; R.B.Kelly
Music: Paul Decha

480a

BENSON (Irregular)

1. God is work-ing his pur-pose out as year succeeds to

year, (Vss. 2, 3, 4) God is work-ing his pur-pose out and the

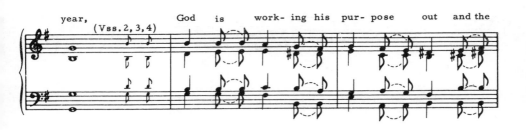

time is draw-ing near; (Vss. 2, 5) near-er and near-er

draws the time, the time that shall sure-ly be, when the

earth shall be filled with the glo- ry of God as the

wa- ters co- ver the sea.

2. From|utmost east to|utmost west where'er man's foot hath|trod,
by the|mouth of many|messengers goes|forth the voice of |God.
'Give|ear to me, ye|continents, ye|isles, give ear to |me,
that the|earth may be filled with the|glory of God as the
|waters cover the|sea.'

3. What can we do to|work God's work, to|prosper and in|crease
the|brotherhood of |all mankind, the|reign of the Prince of|Peace?
What can we do to|hasten the time, the|time that shall surely|be,
when the|earth shall be filled with the|glory of God as the
|waters cover the sea.

4. March we forth in the |strength of God with the|banner of Christ un|furled,
that the|light of the glorious|Gospel of truth may|shine throughout the|world,
fight we the fight with |sorrow and sin, to |set their captives|free,
that the|earth may be filled with the|glory of God as the
|waters cover the|sea.

5. All we can do is|nothing worth un|less God blesses the|deed;
vainly we hope for the|harvest-tide till |God gives life to the|seed;
yet|nearer and nearer|draws the time, the|time that shall surely|be,
when the|earth shall be filled with the|glory of God as the
|waters cover the|sea.

Words: A.C. Ainger (1841-1919)
Music: Millicent D. Kingham (1894)

480 b   PURPOSE (Irregular)

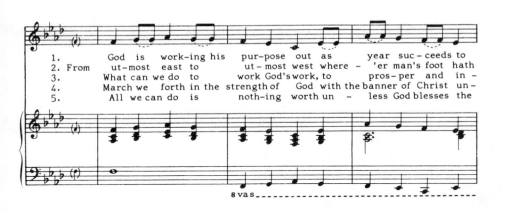

1. God is work-ing his pur-pose out as year suc-ceeds to
2. From ut-most east to ut-most west where - 'er man's foot hath
3. What can we do to work God's work, to pros-per and in -
4. March we forth in the strength of God with the banner of Christ un -
5. All we can do is noth-ing worth un - less God blesses the

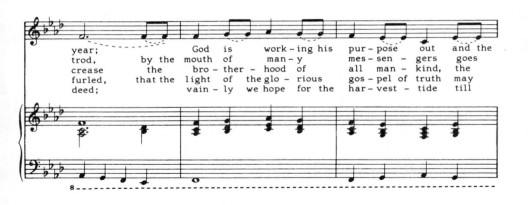

year; God is work - ing his pur - pose out and the
trod, by the mouth of man - y mes - sen - gers goes
crease the bro - ther - hood of all man - kind, the
furled, that the light of the glo - rious gos - pel of truth may
deed; vain - ly we hope for the har - vest - tide till

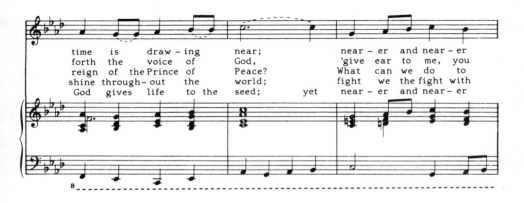

time is draw - ing near; near - er and near - er
forth the voice of God, 'give ear to me, you
reign of the Prince of Peace? What can we do to
shine through-out the world; fight we the fight with
God gives life to the seed; yet near - er and near - er

draws the time, the time that shall sure-ly be, when the
con - ti - nents, you isles, give ear to me, that the
has-ten the time, the time that shall sure-ly be, when the
sor-row and sin to set their cap-tives free, that the
draws the time, the time that shall sure-ly be, when the

earth shall be filled with the glo - ry of God as the
earth may be filled with the glo - ry of God as the
earth shall be filled with the glo - ry of God as the
earth may be filled with the glo - ry of God as the
earth shall be filled with the glo - ry of God as the

wa - ters co - ver the sea.
wa - ters co - ver the sea.'
wa - ters co - ver the sea?
wa - ters co - ver the sea.
wa - ters co - ver the sea.

Words: A.C. Ainger (1841–1919)
Music: Martin Shaw (1875–1958)
Music © Oxford University Press

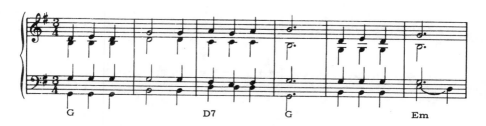

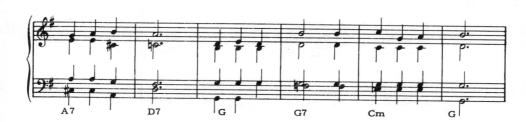

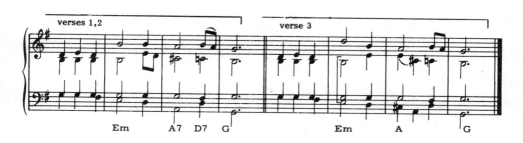

1. God made the birds, their home is the air;
   God made the beasts, each in its lair;
   God made the fish, their home is the sea;
   but God himself is home for me.

2. Birds find their food in their home of air;
   beasts find theirs too, 'most everywhere;
   the fish find theirs in the paths of the sea;
   but God himself is food for me.

3. God loves the birds, they answer in song;
   God loves the beasts, so pow'rfully strong;
   God loves the fish as they swim in the sea;
   but God himself is love for me.

Words: Magnus Wenninger
Music: Paschal Jordan
Harmony: for Celebration Hymnal
        by James O'Donnell

© 1981 Mayhew—McCrimmon Ltd

482

1. God most high of all creation, glory be to you!
   Living God, we come before you, glory be to you!
   Hosts of Heav'n, your praises are singing.
   Shouts of joy and thanks are ringing.
   We on earth re-echo their praises; glory be to you!

2. God of light, our darkness ending, glory be to you!
   God of truth, our doubts dispelling, glory be to you!
   Light of God on all men dawning,
   Christ the rising sun brings morning.
   You have shed your light on our pathway; glory be to you!

3. Mighty God, who brings us freedom, glory be to you!
   Faithful God who keeps his promise, glory be to you!
   As your Church we gather before you,
   and with thanks, we sing and adore you.
   Now made one in Christ, let us praise you; glory be to you!

4. God of love, your ways are gentle, glory be to you!
   God of peace, you heal our sadness, glory be to you!
   Called by you, we hasten to meet you,
   and together pray as we greet you.
   With your loving kindness surround us, glory be to you!

5. Sing your praise to God our Father, glory be to you!
    Praise the Son and Holy Spirit, glory be to you!
    Abba, Father, Lord of creation;
    Jesus Lord, who brought salvation.
    Holy Spirit, dwelling within us, glory be to you!

Words: AELF,
                translated and adapted by Pamela Stotter
Music: Joseph Gelineau

French original ©SEFIM
English words © Pamela Stotter
Music ©1977 SEFIM (C127-1)

REX GLORIAE (87.87.D)

483

1. God, our maker, mighty Father, all creation sings your praise,
    sun and stars in all their splendour, moon in ev'ry changing phase,
    earth with all its trees and grasses, sparkling rivers, ocean blue,
    all unite to pay you homage, singing joyously to you.

2. Provident and wise creator, as your mighty plan unfurled,
    man you made to share your labour in the building of the world.
    Man and woman you created, that united, heart and home,
    they might work and strive together till your endless kingdom come.

3. God of truth and love unbounded, further still your mercy went,
    when uniting earth with heaven, your incarnate Son you sent:
    first-born of your vast creation, holding all in unity,
    leading all in power and wisdom to a glorious destiny.

Words: Denis E. Hurley

© Archdiocese of Durban, South Africa

Music: H. Smart (1813-1879)

484

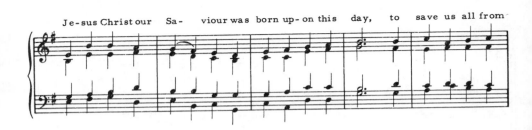

2. In Bethlehem, in Jewry,
   this blessed Babe was born,
   and laid within a manger,
   upon this blessed morn;
   the which his mother Mary,
   did nothing take in scorn.
      O tidings of comfort and joy,
      comfort and joy,
      O tidings of comfort and joy.

3. From God our Heavenly Father,
   a blessed angel came;
   and unto certain shepherds
   brought tidings of the same:
   How that in Bethlehem was born
   the Son of God by name:
      O tidings of . . .

4. 'Fear not then,' said the angel,
   'let nothing you affright,
   this day is born a Saviour
   of a pure Virgin bright,
   to free all those who trust in him
   from Satan's power and might.'
      O tidings of . . .

5. The shepherds at those tidings
   rejoiced much in mind,
   and left their flocks a-feeding,
   in tempest, storm, and wind;
   and went to Bethlehem straightway,
   the Son of God to find.
      O tidings of . . .

6. And when they came to Bethlehem
   where our dear Saviour lay,
   they found him in a manger,
   where oxen feed on hay;
   his mother Mary kneeling down,
   unto the Lord did pray.
      O tidings of . . .

7. Now to the Lord sing praises,
   all you within this place,
   and with true love and brotherhood
   each other now embrace;
   this holy tide of Christmas
   all other doth deface.
      O tidings of . . .

Words: Traditional English Carol
Music: Traditional, arranged by
       Roger Humphrey

Arrangement © 1983 Mayhew-McCrimmon Ltd

485

God's Spirit precedes us,
guides and gently leads us.
Alleluia, alleluia!
God's Spirit precedes us,
guides and gently leads us.
Alleluia, alleluia!

1. Through mountains and valleys he journeys with us,
    all his work entrusts to our control;
    and those who know not what God wants from them
    must silently wait on the voice of our God.

2. In sorrow and gladness, he's always near us,
    and his love, he gives to everyone;
    and those who know not God's presence with them
    must just take a look at the life all around.

Words: translated by Bonaventure Hinwood

Dutch original ©Bmg-Music, Holland

English arrangement ©Bonaventure Hinwood

Harmony: for Celebration Hymnal
by John Rombaut

©1981 Mayhew-McCrimmon Ltd

VULPIUS (888 + Alleluias)

1. Good Christ- ian men, re- joice and sing!

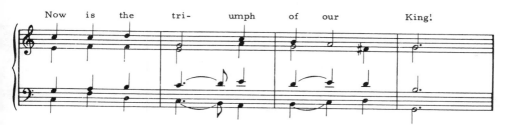

Now is the tri- umph of our King!

To all the world glad news we bring:

Al- le- lu- ia! Al- le- lu- ia! Al- le- lu- ia!

Another harmonisation can be found at Hymn 424

2. The Lord of Life is risen for ay:
bring flowers of song to strew his way;
let all mankind rejoice and say: Alleluia!

3. Praise we in songs of victory
that Love, that Life, which cannot die,
and sing with hearts uplifted high: Alleluia!

4. Thy name we bless, O risen Lord,
and sing today with one accord
the life laid down, the life restored: Alleluia!

Words: C. A. Alington
Music: M. Vulpius, Gesangbuch, 1609,
harmonized by F. Layriz (1844)

487

D   A   G   D   A7   D

Bm   G   A   Bm   F♯m   Bm

F♯m   Em   A   Bm   Em   A7   D   G   D

1.   Good Lady Poverty, come be my bride;
   forever you and me, walk side by side.
   Teach me your wisdom, lead me your way.
   Show me the path you take and walk with Christ each day.

2.   Good Lady Poverty, so filled with grace;
   such sweet humility shines from your face.
   You have no pride or vanity.
   Great daughter of the Lord, his love has made you free.

3.   Good Lady Poverty, I sing your praise.
   St. Francis, blessed one, has walked your ways.
   He sang your virtues; you were his prize.
   Good Lady Poverty, an angel in disguise.

Words and music: Sebastian Temple

© Franciscan Communications Centre

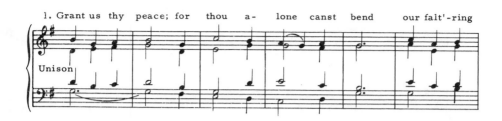

1. Grant us thy peace; for thou a- lone canst bend our falt'-ring

Unison

pur- pose to a no- bler end; thy love a- lone can teach our

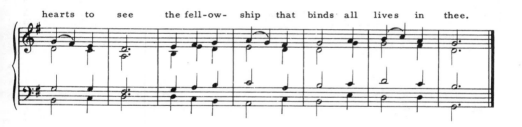

hearts to see the fell-ow- ship that binds all lives in thee.

2. Grant us thy peace; for men have filled the years
with greed and envy and with foolish fears,
with squandered treasures and ignoble gain,
and fruitless harvests that we reap in vain.

3. Grant us thy peace; till all our strife shall seem
the hateful memory of some evil dream;
till that new song ring out that shall not cease,
'In heaven thy glory and on earth thy peace!'

Words: J.H.B. Masterman 1867-1933
Music: © John Ainslie

489

Refrain

Great-er love has no man than this: that he gave his life for his friends.

Em ... Am ... fine ... Verses

B ... Em

1. Now I

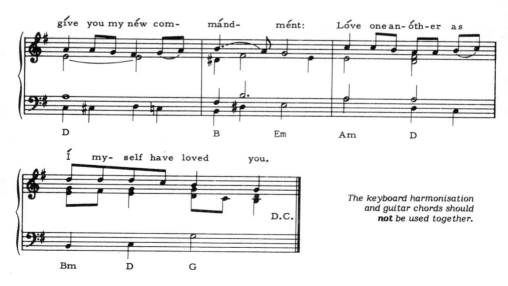

give you my new com- mánd- ment: Lóve one an- óth-er as

D ... B ... Em ... Am ... D

Í my- self have loved you.

Bm ... D ... G ... D.C.

*The keyboard harmonisation and guitar chords should **not** be used together.*

* 2.   Yóu will be my fríends if you fóllow my précept:
     Love one another as I myself have loved you.

3.   As the Fáther loves me álways, so álso have I lóved you:
    Love one another as I myself have loved you.

4.   Be cónstant in my lóve and fóllow my commándment.
    Love one another as I myself have loved you.

5.   And appróaching my Passóver I have lóved you to the énd.
    Love one another as I myself have loved you.

6.   By thís shall men knów that yóu are my discíples.
    Love one another as I myself have loved you.

*The metre of the verses is irregular, but if the accents are followed
it will not be difficult to fit the words to the music.
Verse 2* omits the first note.*

Words: John 14
       arranged by Helena Scott
Music: Jose Weber

490

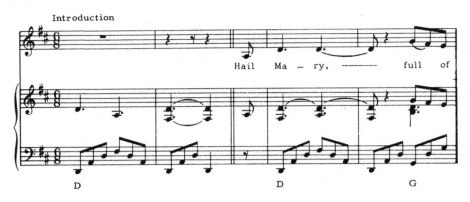

Introduction

Hail Ma — ry, ———— full of

grace,———— the Lord ———— is with you.————

blessed are you a — mong wo — men, and blest is the fruit
of your

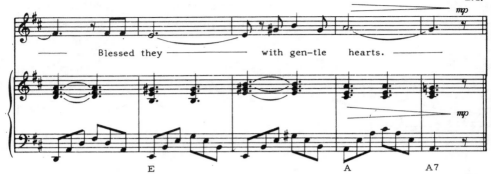

mp

Blessed they ———— with gen-tle hearts. ————

E   A   A7

mp

Hail Mary, full of grace,
the Lord is with you.
Blessed are you among women,
and blest is the fruit of your womb, Jesus.
Holy Mary, Mother of God,
pray for us sinners
now and at the hour of death.
Amen.

**Gentle woman, quiet light,
morning star, so strong and bright,
gentle mother, peaceful dove,
teach us wisdom; teach us love.**

1. You were chosen by the Father;
    you were chosen for the Son.
    You were chosen from all women,
    and for women, shining one.

2. Blessed are you, among women.
    Blest in turn all women too.
    Blessed they with gentle spirits.
    Blessed they with gentle hearts.

Words: based on Luke 1:28
       by Carey Landry
Music: Carey Landry

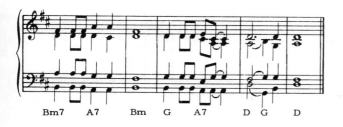

1. Hail Mary, full of grace.
   The Lord is with thee.
   Blessed art thou among women,
   and blessed is the fruit of thy womb, Jesus.

2. Holy Mary, Mother of God,
   pray for us, sinners,
   now and at the hour of death;
   pray for us sinners now. Amen.

Words: Tradition (Luke 1:28ff.)
adapted by Mary Lu Walker
Music: Mary Lu Walker

© 1975 Missionary Society of St Paul the Apostle
in the State of New York

Harmony: for Celebration Hymnal
by Eric Welch

© 1981 Mayhew—McCrimmon Ltd

492

IN DER WIEGEN (86 866)

*Chords should **not** be played with this arrangement

1. Hail Mary, mother of our God,
   a lamp that always burns;
   for you the angels keep a feast,
   from you all evil turns,
   from you all evil turns.

2. It's thanks to you God's only Son
   in darkness shed his light;
   it's thanks to you that sinful man
   rejoiced to know what's right,
   rejoiced to know what's right.

3. You gave a place within your womb
   to him who knows no bound;
   a virgin yet a mother too,
   in you his home he found,
   in you his home he found.

4. It's thanks to you creation came
   to know what's good and true;
   God calls his servant 'mother' now –
   no other maid but you,
   no other maid but you!

Words: Willard F.Jabusch
Music: Melody from Corner's Geistliche
Nachtigall (1649)

© 1966 Willard F.Jabusch

493

1. He is Lord, he is Lord.
He is ri-sen from the dead and he is Lord.
Ev-'ry knee shall bow, ev-'ry tongue con-fess that Je-sus Christ is Lord.

2. He is King, he is King.
He is risen from the dead and he is King.
Ev'ry knee shall bow, ev'ry tongue confess
that Jesus Christ is King.

3. He is love, he is love.
He is risen from the dead and he is love.
Ev'ry knee shall bow, ev'ry tongue confess
that Jesus Christ is love.

Words and Music: Unknown, arranged by Rosalind Pitcher

Arrangement © Mayhew-McCrimmon Ltd

494

Chorus
He is ri- sen, al- le-lu- ia, al- le-lu- ia!

E   A   E   D   E

He is ri- sen, al- le-lu- ia, al- le-lu- ia!

Fine

A   E   D   E

1. Cry out with joy to the Lord, all the earth, al- le-lu- ia!

A   E   D   E

Serve the Lord with glad- ness, al- le-lu- ia!

A   E   D   E

Come be-fore him, sing-ing for joy, al- le- lu- ia!

A   E   D   E   G   D   E

D.C.

2. Know that he, the Lord, is God, alleluia.
   He made us, we belong to him, alleluia.
   We are his people, the sheep of his flock, alleluia.

3. Go within his gates giving thanks, alleluia.
   Enter his courts with songs of praise, alleluia.
   Give thanks to him and bless his name, alleluia.

4. Indeed, how good is the Lord, alleluia.
   Eternal his merciful love, alleluia.
   He is faithful from age to age, alleluia.

5. Glory to the Father and Son, alleluia.
   And to the Spirit with them one, alleluia.
   As it was and ever shall be one God for eternity.

Words: Psalm 99
Music: Sebastian Temple,
       harmonised by Stephen Dean

Words © The Grail (England)
Music © Mayhew—McCrimmon Ltd

495

1. He is risen, tell the story to the nations of the night;
   from their sin and from their blindness, let them walk in Easter light.
   Now begins a new creation,
   now has come our true salvation.
   Jesus Christ, the Son of God!

2. Mary goes to tell the others of the wonders she has seen;
   John and Peter come a'running – what can all this truly mean?
   O Rabboni, Master holy,
   to appear to one so lowly!
   Jesus Christ, the Son of God!

3. He has cut down death and evil, he has conquered all despair;
   he has lifted from our shoulders, all the weight of anxious care.
   Risen Brother, now before you,
   we will worship and adore you.
   Jesus Christ, the Son of God!

4. Now get busy, bring the message, so that all may come to know
   there is hope for saint and sinner, for our God has loved us so.
   Ev'ry church bell is a'ringing,
   ev'ry Christian now is singing.
   Jesus Christ, the Son of God!

Words: Willard F. Jabusch
Music: Polish traditional

At a moderate speed

He's a most un-us-u-al man, he

Em Am   Em Am   Em   C   D   Em

the
makes crowds all stop and stare, he tea-ches people how care, he

C   D   G   Em   Am

to
tea-ches peo-ple how share. He has no place to lay his head, his home is ev'ry-

Em   Am   Em   C   D   Em   Am

2. He's a most unusual man, he makes the stormy days turn fine,
   he changes water into wine, he gives his body as a sign.
   And he died that we might live, his life is yours and mine.
   Follow if you can, this most unusual man,
   follow if you can, this most unusual man.

3. He's a most unusual man, as rich and poor as a man can be,
   he came to set the prisoners free, he came to make the blind men see.
   And he gave the world this message, "Come and follow me."
   Follow if you can, this most unusual man,
   follow if you can, this most unusual man.

Words: Wendy Poussard
Music: Christopher Willcock

1. Help us accept each other as Christ accepted us;
   teach us as sister, brother, each person to embrace.
   Be present, Lord among us and bring us to believe
   we are ourselves accepted and meant to love and live.

2. Teach us, O Lord, your lessons, as in our daily life
   we struggle to be human and search for hope and faith.
   Teach us to care for people, for all not just for some,
   to love them as we find them or as they may become.

3. Let your acceptance change us, so that we may be moved
   in living situations to do the truth in love;
   to practice your acceptance until we know by heart
   the table of forgiveness and laughter's healing art.

4. Lord, for today's encounters with all who are in need,
   who hunger for acceptance, for righteousness and bread,
   we need new eyes for seeing, new hands for holding on:
   renew us with your Spirit; Lord, free us, make us one!

Words: Fred Kaan
Music: Doreen Potter

498 LITTLE CORNARD (66.66.88)

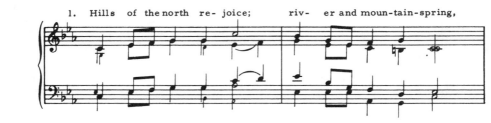

1. Hills of the north re- joice; riv- er and moun-tain-spring,

hark to the ad- vent voice; val- ley and low- land, sing:

though ab- sent long, your Lord is nigh; he judge-ment brings and

vic- tor- y.

Words: C.E. Oakley
Music: Martin Shaw

© J. Curwen & Sons, Ltd

2. Isles of the southern seas,
   deep in your coral caves
   pent be each warring breeze,
   lulled be your restless waves:
   He comes to reign with boundless sway,
   and makes your wastes his great highway.

3. Lands of the east, awake,
   soon shall your sons be free;
   the sleep of ages break,
   and rise to liberty.
   On your far hills, long cold and grey,
   has dawned the everlasting day.

4. Shores of the utmost west,
   ye that have waited long,
   unvisited, unblest,
   break forth to swelling song;
   high raise the note, that Jesus died,
   yet lives and reigns, the Crucified.

5. Shout, while ye journey home;
   songs be in every mouth;
   lo, from the north we come,
   from east and west and south.
   City of God, the bonds are free,
   we come to live and reign in thee!

499

1. His light now shines in the darkness a - bout us, his light now shines and the
Refrain. His name is love and he gives himself to us, his name is love and he

Verse ending

Refrain ending

Fine

dark-ness has gone.　　His　makes us his own.

This song should not have any harmonic accompaniment. Please resist the temptation to add 'Western' harmonies. Instead it should be accompanied by untuned percussion and spontaneous vocal harmony.

1. His light now shines in the darkness about us,
   his light now shines and the darkness has gone.

   His name is love and he gives himself to us;
   his name is love, and he makes us his own.

2. His love is warm like the sun of the morning,
   his love is warm like the promise of dawn.

3. His love surrounds like a mother's devotion,
   he meets our needs when awake and asleep.

4. How can we answer the love that he shows us,
   what can we do to respond to his care?

5. Receive his love and reflect it to others,
   do all for them as he does all for you.

6. For when we know him, we give ourselves to them,
   and when we love him, we give them our all.

Words: Tom Colvin
Music: Gonja Folk Song
　　　Adapted by Tom Colvin

500

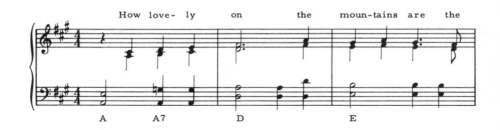

2. You watchmen, lift your voices joyfully as one,
   shout for your king, your king!
   See eye to eye, the Lord restoring Sion:
   Our God reigns . . .

3. Wasteplaces of Jerusalem, break forth with joy!
   We are redeemed, redeemed,
   The Lord has saved and comforted his people.
   Our God reigns . . .

4. Ends of the earth, see the salvation of our God!
   Jesus is Lord, is Lord!
   Before the nations, he has bared his holy arm.
   Our God reigns . . .

Words and Music: Leonard E. Smith, Jr.

501

1. I am the Bread of life. He who comes to me shall not

hun - ger, he who be - lieves in me shall not thirst.

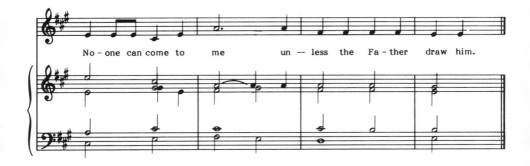

No - one can come to me un — less the Fa - ther draw him.

Chorus

And I will raise him up, and I will raise him up, and I will raise him up on the last day.

2. The **bread** that I will **give**
is my **flesh** for the life of the **world**,
and he who **eats of** this **bread**,
he shall **live** for ever,
he shall live for ever. *(Jn.6:50-51)*

3. Unless you eat
of the **flesh** of the Son of **Man**,
and **drink of** his **blood**,
and **drink of** his **blood**,
you **shall** not have life within you. *(Jn.6:53)*

4. For my **flesh** is **food** indeed,
and my **blood** is drink **indeed**.
He who **eats of** my **flesh**
and **drinks of** my **blood**
abides in me. *(Jn.6:55-56)*

5. Yes, **Lord**, I/we believe,
that **you** are the **Christ**,
the **Son** of **God**,
who have **come**
into the **world**. *(Jn.11:27)*

Words: John (passim)
arranged by Suzanne Toolan
Music: Suzanne Toolan

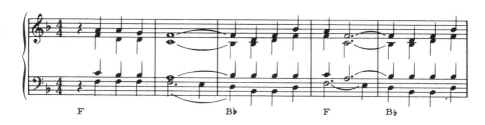

F   B♭   F   B♭

Instrumental

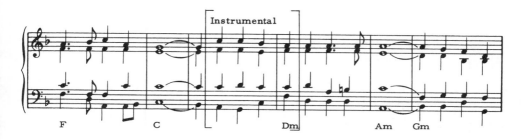

F   C   Dm   Am   Gm

F   B♭   F   C7   F

1.   I am the vine, you are the branches:
no one can live apart from me.
Cut off from me you can do nothing:
yet joined with me, all things are yours.

2.   You are the fruit borne by my Father,
who tends and cares for every limb.
Be not afraid: he will not harm you.
Your fear he'll prune, and set you free.

3.   Remain in me: keep my commandments.
My love for you led me to die.
Hold fast to me: I'll never leave you,
in life, in death, I'll love you still.

Words: paraphrased from John 15
       by John Glynn
Music: John Glynn

© 1979 John Glynn

Harmony: for Celebration Hymnal
       by Eric Welch

© 1981 Mayhew-McCrimmon Ltd

503

B   E   A   E   A   E   B   E   B

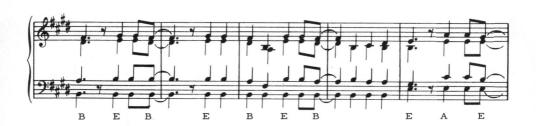

B   E   B   E   B   E   B   E   A   E

1, 3

A   E   B   E   B   E

2, 4 Interlude (after verses 2 & 4)

(E)   G♯   DC♯m   F♯m

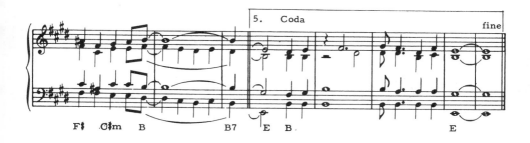

1. I heard the Lord call my name,
   listen close, you'll hear the same;
   I heard the Lord call my name,
   listen close, you'll hear the same;
   I heard the Lord, call my name,
   listen close, you'll hear the same.
   Take his hand, we are glory bound.

2. His word is love, love's the word,
   that's the message that I heard;
   (three times, then:-)
   Take his hand, we are glory bound.

   Place your hand in his and you will know;
   he will show you where to go.

3. I felt his love from above
   settle on me like a dove;
   (three times, then:-)
   Take his hand, we are glory bound.

4. And to the Father, all your days,
   with the Son and Spirit, praise;
   (three times, then:-)
   Take his hand, we are glory bound.

   Place your hand in his and you will know;
   he will show you where to go.

5. I heard the Lord call my name,
   listen close, you'll hear the same;
   (three times, then:-)
   Take his hand, we are glory bound.
   Take his hand, we are glory bound.

Words and Music: Jacob Krieger

I heard the Lord © 1973 The Word of God
All rights reserved. Used by permission.

Harmony: for Celebration Hymnal
            by Frances M. & Robert B.Kelly
© Mayhew—McCrimmon Ltd

504

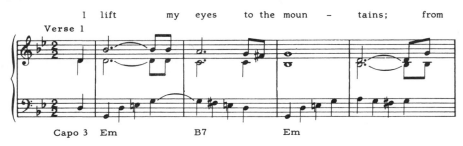

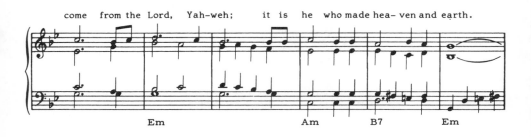

Words:
based on Psalm 12(
by Gregory Norbert
Music:
Gregory Norbert

Verses

CANTOR

He will not al- low you to stum- ble.

Our God keeps watch

He keeps all ev- il a- way from you.

1 He nev- er sleeps, but stands watch o- ver you.

2 like a shad- ow he cov- ers you.

3 He takes you un- der his pro- tec- tion.

ALL THE LORD WHO MADE BOTH HEAV'N AND EARTH

To Resp
(previc
page)

* n.b. *After verse 3 and its Response, the Psalm ends with*
the Antiphon and Response once more.

Words, based on Psalm 120(121): Huub Oosterhuis, translated by Tony Barr
Music: Bernard Huijbers

506

I met you at the
cross, Jes – us my Lord;
heard you from that cross: my name you

called –   asked me to fol-low you   all of my days,

B(sus4)   B   A   E

asked me for ev – er   more   your name to   praise.

A   Am   E   B(sus4)   E   (D♯

last time only

C♯   B Bass)   E

2.   I saw you on the cross
     dying for me;
     I put you on that cross:
     but your one plea –
     Would I now follow you all of my days,
     and would I evermore your great name
                               praise?

3.   Jesus, my Lord and King,
     Saviour cf all,
     Jesus the King of kings,
     you heard my call –
     That I would follow you all of my days,
     and that for evermore your name I'd
                               praise.

507

Verse
saw a star up high a-bove the hea-vens. I heard the an-gels sing-ing in the
sky. I watched the shepherds coming from the sheep-fold. I
e-ven thought I heard a ba-by cry. No-one there would lis-ten to my
sto-ry, and no-one seemed to care a-bout the child;

2. I saw a star shine down upon the stable.
   I watched the kings and gifts go riding by.
   I crept up close and looked into the manger
   and it was then I heard a baby cry. But ...

3. I hurried home and there I met the townsfolk.
   I wandered in the hills and all around.
   I tried to tell my friends about the story
   of Angels, Shepherds, Kings and Babe I'd found.
   But all alone I knelt before that manger,
   the sheep and cows and oxen standing by;
   and he was beautiful –
   the baby born to save us,
   as in his mother's arms he gently lay.
   Yes, he was beautiful,
   the baby Jesus born on Christmas Day.

Words: Joan McCrimmon

© Mayhew-McCrimmon Ltd

Music: Roger Whittaker

© Tembo Music Ltd

508

Introduction With majesty ♩ = 80

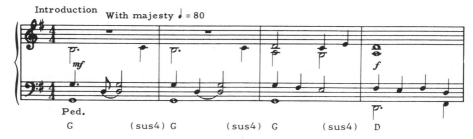

G   (sus4) G   (sus4) G   (sus4) D

Verse
1. I, the Lord of sea and sky, I have heard my peo-ple cry.

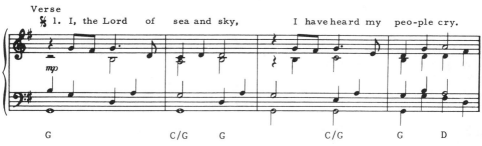

G   C/G   G   C/G   G   D

All who dwell in dark- and sin my hand will save.

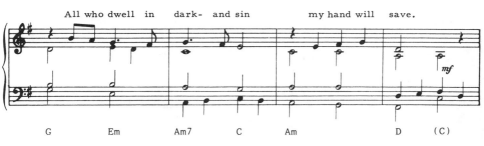

G   Em   Am7   C   Am   D   (C)

2. I, the Lord of snow and rain,
   I have borne my people's pain.
   I have wept for love of them.
   They turn away.
   I will break their hearts of stone,
   give them hearts for love alone.
   I will speak my word to them.
   Whom shall I send?

3. I, the Lord of wind and flame,
   I will tend the poor and lame.
   I will set a feast for them.
   My hand will save.
   Finest bread I will provide
   till their hearts be satisfied.
   I will give my life to them.
   Whom shall I send?

Words: Based on Isaiah 6, Dan Schutte, S.J.
Music: Dan Schutte, S.J., arranged by Michael Pope, S.J.
       Dan Schutte, S.J., John Weissrock.

1. I was born before creation,
   when the world was yet to be.
   From the dawn of time uncounted
   I have sung God's melody.

   I am Wisdom, his companion,
   ever at his side to be;
   I delight in his creating,
   never ending, ever free.

2. Ev'ry sea and ev'ry river
   I have seen them come to birth;
   for the hills and for the mountains
   seen him raise the virgin earth.

3. There were stars hung in the heavens,
   and the clouds were in his plan:
   but the time I'll ever cherish
   was the day he formed a man.

4. Never has he ceased creating,
   and I'm with him to this day;
   so I'm glad to see his image
   in the people of today.

Words: based on Proverbs 8:22-31
    by John Glynn
Music: John Glynn

© 1978 John Glynn

Harmony: for Celebration Hymnal
    by John Rombaut

© 1981 Mayhew-McCrimmon Ltd

510

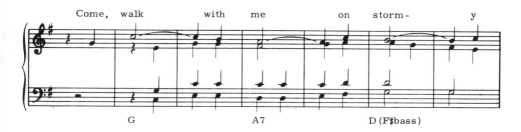

Come, walk with me on storm- y

G   A7   D (F♯bass)

wa- ters. Why fear? Reach out, and

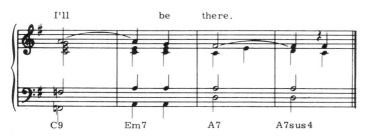

Bm   G   D (F♯bass)

I'll be there.

C9   Em7   A7   A7sus4

2. And you, my friend, will you now leave me,
   or do you know me as your Lord?

3. Your life will be transformed with power
   by living truly in my name.

4. And if you say: 'Yes, Lord, I love you, '
   then feed my lambs and feed my sheep.

Words and Music: Gerard Markland
© Kevin Mayhew Ltd

511

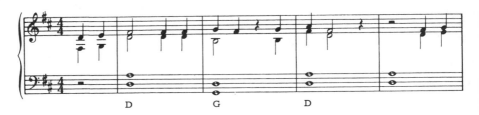

1. I will never forget you, my people,
   I have carved you on the palm of my hand.
   I will never forget you;
   I will not leave you orphaned.
   I will never forget my own.

2. Does a mother forget her baby?
   Or a woman the child within her womb?
   Yet, even if these forget,
   yes, even if these forget,
   I will never forget my own.

   Repeat Verse 1

1. I will sing, I will sing a song un-to the Lord. I will

sing, I will sing a song un-to the Lord. I will

sing, I will sing a song un-to the Lord. Al- le-

lu- ia, glo- ry to the Lord.

Chorus (same melody as verses)

Allelu, alleluia, glory to the Lord, (3)
alleluia, glory to the Lord.

2. We will come, we will come as one
    before the Lord. (3)
    Alleluia, glory to the Lord.

3. If the Son, if the Son shall make
    you free, (3)
    you shall be free indeed.

4. They that sow in tears shall reap
    in joy. (3)
    Alleluia, glory to the Lord.

5. Ev'ry knee shall bow and ev'ry
    tongue confess (3)
    that Jesus Christ is Lord.

6. In his name, in his name we have
    the victory. (3)
    Alleluia, glory to the Lord.

Words and Music: Max Dyer, arranged for Celebration Hymnal by Stephen Dean

513

Refrain

Verse

I will tell of your love for me always, Lord;
I will tell of your goodness to me.

1. Ev'ry morning the sun comes shining through
   to tell me a new day is born;
   and I feel a joy rising in my heart,
   the joy of life that comes from you.

2. Ev'ry mountain and hill that you have made
   tells me how strong you are;
   and I feel a pow'r rising in my heart,
   the pow'r of strength that comes from you.

3. Ev'ry flower that lifts its head to me
   tells me how gentle you are;
   and I feel a joy rising in my heart,
   the joy of love that comes from you.

4. As the darkness comes on at close of day
   it tells me you watch through the night;
   and I feel a longing rising in my heart,
   a longing to be one with you.

Words and music: Sister Marie Lydia Pereira
Arrangement: for Celebration Hymnal
by John Rombaut

© 1981 Mayhew—McCrimmon Ltd

Refrain

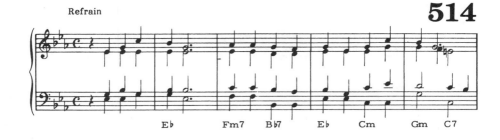

Eb   Fm7   Bb7   Eb   Cm   Gm   C7

Verse

Fm   Bb7   Eb   Fm7   Bb7   Gm   C7

Fm7   Bb7   Eb   Fm   G   Cm   Eb7   Ab6   Bb7   Eb

I'll sing God's praises, now and evermore.
I'll sing God's praises, now and evermore.

1.   He is my guide and my shepherd,
     now and evermore.
     He gives me rest in green pastures,
     now and evermore.

2.   Near restful waters he leads me,
     now and evermore.
     Along the right path he keeps me,
     now and evermore.

3.   His rod and crook are my comfort,
     now and evermore.
     With oil my head is anointed,
     now and evermore.

4.   His loving favours pursue me,
     now and evermore.
     His house, my dwelling for ever,
     now and evermore.

Words: based on Psalm *22(23)*
        by Aniceto Nazareth
Music: Aniceto Nazareth

©1980 Aniceto Nazareth,
St Pius College, Bombay 63

515

The chorus is sung rhythmically, not too fast. The verses should be sung faster by a leader or small group.
The melody is the middle notes of the top stave. Chords in brackets should be played on Capo 3.

Chorus
If God is for us, who can be a-gainst,

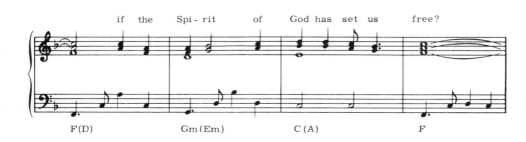

F(D)　　　　Gm(Em)　　　　C(A)

if the Spi-rit of God has set us free?

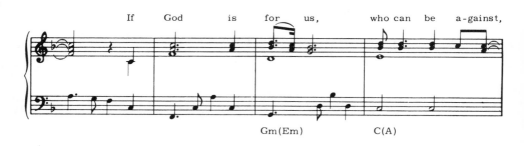

F(D)　　　　Gm(Em)　　　　C(A)　　　　F

If God is for us, who can be a-gainst,

Gm(Em)　　　　C(A)

if the Spi-rit of God has set us free?

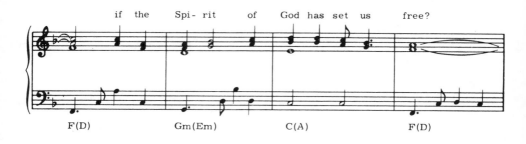

F(D)　　　　Gm(Em)　　　　C(A)　　　　F(D)

Verse

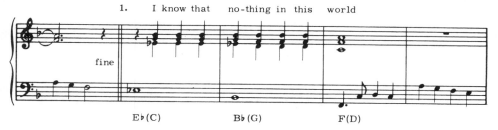

2. Nothing can take us from his love,
   poured out in Jesus, the Lord.

3. And nothing present or to come
   can ever take us from his love.

4. I know that neither death nor life
   can ever take us from his love.

Words, from Romans 8: 31-39, and Music: John Foley, S.J.

516 AURELIA (7 6.7 6.D)

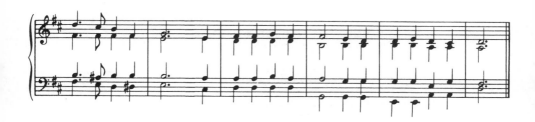

1. If God is our defender, who will th' accuser be?
   His only Son he spared not, but gave him graciously.
   When God himself grants pardon, who ventures to condemn?
   Will Jesus Christ, the Saviour, who died and rose for men?

2. Can anything divide us from that most loving Lord?
   Can pain, or tribulation? Can famine, peril, sword?
   No, none of these can cause us from his great love to fall;
   for by the strength he gave us, we triumph over all.

3. Of this we can be certain, and sing with every breath:
   that nought that is, or will be, and neither life nor death,
   and nothing in creation, below us or above,
   can tear us from Christ Jesus, and from his Father's love.

Words: based on Romans 8
by Denis E.Hurley
© Archdiocese of Durban

Music: Samuel S.Wesley (1810–76)

Verse

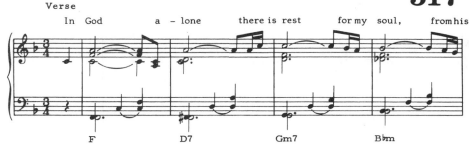

In God a – lone there is rest for my soul, from his

F   D7   Gm7   B♭m

care comes my safe-ty in life. With him a–

Dm   G7   Csus4   C7   F

lone for my rock and my for-tress, this I know I will ne-ver fall

D7   Gm7   B♭m   F   C6   C7

Refrain

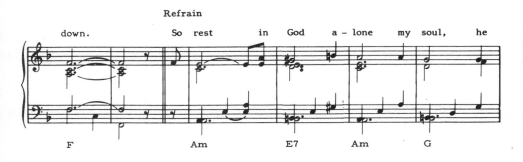

down. So rest in God a – lone my soul, he

F   Am   E7   Am   G

is   the source   of my hope.

C   G7   C   C+

2. In God I find my shelter, my strength
   all you people do rely on him.
   Unburden your hearts to the Lord your God,
   at all times he will listen to you.

3. Beware of those who will scoff at our God;
   their intent is to misguide your way.
   We trust alone in the rock of our safety
   and we know we will never lose hope.

Words: based on Psalm 70
by Douglas Rowe
Music: Douglas Rowe
Harmony: for Celebration Hymnal
by John Rombaut

1. 2. 3. | Final ending

instrumental

In the beginning all was empty and void;
God's spirit moved above the waters.
Out of the darkness came a word that brought new life;
'This is so good, let there be light.'

1. Then in the stillness of the night your Word
   leapt into our city of turmoil;
   a man was born, a man of peace and not of war,
   revealing hopes yet unfulfilled.

2. Jesus, his name and what a gift he was,
   inspired to know the Father's vision.
   And he so loved us more than his own life.
   What greater gift could he have shared.

3. So we are called to give flesh to our word
   and be creators with the Spirit.
   Wonder will be the sign that we are on the way,
   sharing our hope, alive our word.

Words and music: Gregory Norbert OSB

519

Unison

The metre of this song is irregular; the note values in the melody
apply to verse 1. However, it is not difficult to fit the other verses.

1. It's a long hard journey,
   and the road keeps turning
   and we just keep travelling on;
   the signs aren't clear enough,
   the ends aren't near enough,
   and half our time is gone.

   O, the Lord sends troubles,
   the Lord sends trials,
   the Lord sends a heavy load.
   But he'll keep on leading us
   and keep on guiding us
   as long as we're trav'ling his road,
   as long as we're trav'ling his road.

2. With so many days to live,
   it's hard for life to give
   a meaning mile after mile.
   The roads keep crossing,
   and the coins we're tossing
   choose the path in a visionless style

3. Though we walk as brothers,
   still we hurt each other,
   and our love turns to acid and stone.
   Though we're hand in hand
   we don't understand
   that no one's walking alone.

4. Well, he never told us
   that the road before us
   would be smooth or simple or clear.
   But he set us singing
   and our hope keeps springing
   and we're raised from hating and fear.

5. Well, the road is ours
   with its rocks and flowers
   and mica gleams in the stone.
   Well, there's joy awaiting
   in the celebrating
   that we're never walking alone.

Words and music:
   Nick Hodson
   © The Liturgical
      Conference, USA

Harmony: Erik Routley

©1975 Erik Routley

520

It's good to give thanks to the Lord, de – clare your love in the

D   G   D   G

mor – ning; the lute will sound a new chord, the me – lo – dy a–

D   G   D   G

Refrain

dorn – ing! And you, O Lord, have made me glad; for all your

G   D   G   A   F♯m   Bm   Em

works I'll be sing – ing, the righ–teous flou – rish like the grass which

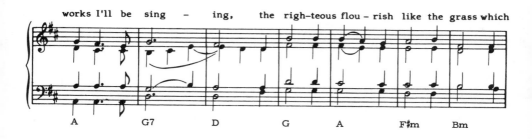

A   G7   D   G   A   F♯m   Bm

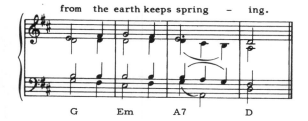

1. It's good to give thanks to the Lord, declare your love in the morning;
   the lute will sound a new chord, the melody adorning!

   **And you, O Lord, have made me glad; for all your works I'll be singing;
   the righteous flourishing like the grass which from the earth keeps springing.**

2. They're planted in God's own abode, in God's own house they will flourish;
   they'll still bear fruit when they're old, for God will tend and nourish!

3. Sing glory to God up above, the Son of God, our dear Saviour,
   and to the Spirit of Love, whose care will never waver!

Words: Psalm 92
         paraphrase by John Ylvisaker
Music: John Ylvisaker

©1979 John C. Ylvisaker

Harmony: for Celebration Hymnal
         by John Rombaut

©1981 Mayhew—McCrimmon Ltd

521

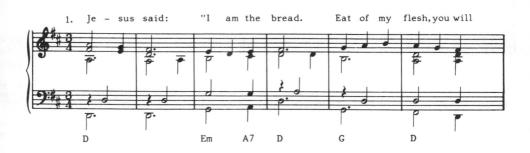

1. Je - sus said: "I am the bread. Eat of my flesh, you will

D   Em   A7   D   G   D

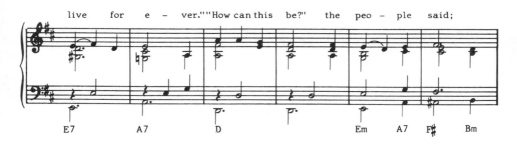

live   for   e - ver.""How can this   be?"   the peo - ple   said;

E7   A7   D   Em   A7   F♯   Bm

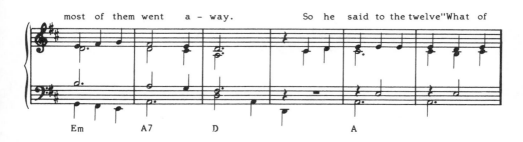

most of them went   a - way.   So   he   said to the twelve"What of

Em   A7   D   A

Chorus

you?"   and this is the   an-swer they gave,   say - ing:"Lord, to

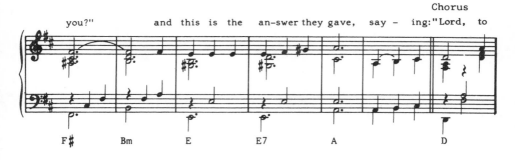

F♯   Bm   E   E7   A   D

whom shall we go? You have the words of e –

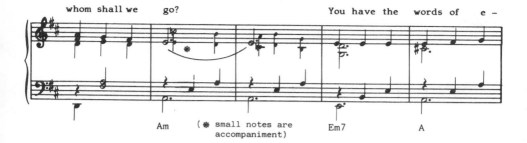

Am (✱ small notes are accompaniment) Em7 A

– ter – nal life. Lord, to whom shall we go?

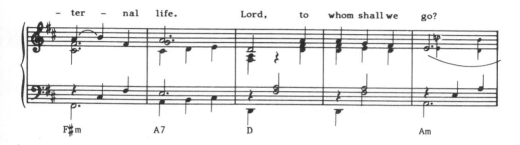

F♯m A7 D Am

You have the mess–age of life."

Em7 A7 D

2. Jesus said: "I came from heaven.
   I give my flesh for the life of the world."
   "This man is mad!" the people said;
   slowly, they went away.
   So he said to the twelve "What of you?"
   And this is the answer they gave, saying:

3. Jesus said: "I have seen God.
   Eat of my body and you too will see him."
   "This is not true!" the people said;
   angry, they went away.
   So he said to the twelve "What of you?"
   And this is the answer they gave, saying:

Words and Music © Stephen Dean

522

Refrain
Je- sus, the ho- ly lamb of God, car-ried the

cross for me. Je- sus, the ho- ly

Lamb of God, died that I might be | 1st time free.

Last time free. | Verse 1.He who is God made himself low: a

ser- vant   and hum-bler   yet.   He bowed   his

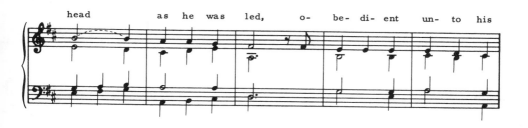

head   as he was   led,   o- be- di- ent un- to his

death.

2. Therefore has God raised him on high
   and named him our Saviour and Lord;
   all knees will bend
   in praise without end
   to Jesus for ever adored.

Words: based on Philippians 2: 6-11, by Briege O'Hare
Music: Briege O'Hare, harmonised by Rosalind Pitcher

523

YISU NE KAHA

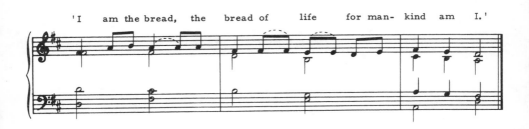

2. Jesus the Lord said, 'I am the door,
   the way and the door for the poor am I,
   the way and the door for the poor am I,
   the way and the door for the poor am I. '
   Jesus the Lord said, 'I am the door,
   the way and the door for the poor am I. '

3. Jesus the Lord said, 'I am the light,
   the one true light of the world am I,
   the one true light of the world am I,
   the one true light of the world am I. '
   Jesus the Lord said, 'I am the light,
   the one true light of the world am I. '

4. Jesus the Lord said, 'I am the shepherd,
   the one good shepherd of the sheep am I,
   the one good shepherd of the sheep am I,
   the one good shepherd of the sheep am I. '
   Jesus the Lord said, 'I am the shepherd,
   the one good shepherd of the sheep am I. '

5. Jesus the Lord said, 'I am the life,
   the resurrection and the life am I,
   the resurrection and the life am I,
   the resurrection and the life am I. '
   Jesus the Lord said, 'I am the life,
   the resurrection and the life am I. '

Words: Anonymous, Urdu translated by Dermott Monahan (1906-57)
Music: Urdu melody, 'Yisu Ne Kaha', harmonised by
   Francis Brotherton Westbrook (1903-75)

Words by permission Methodist Church Division of Education & Youth, London.
Music © Oxford University Press.

1. Jesus the Word has lived among us,
    sharing his fulness, truth and grace,
    God's only Son, the Father's loved one
    reveals him to the human race.
    Jesus the Word has lived among us
    sharing his fullness, truth and grace.

2. He was with God from the beginning
    and through him all things came to be.
    He lightens darkness, conquers evil,
    gives life for living, glad and free.
    He was with God from the beginning
    and through him all things came to be.

3. Sing praise to God who sent Christ Jesus
    to be his sign of endless love;
    sent him to live his life among us,
    lifting our hearts to things above.
    Sing praise to God who sent Christ Jesus
    to be his sign of endless love!

Words: John 1 & 3
paraphrased by Keith D. Pearson
Music: Traditional French Carol

©1976 Joint Board of Christian Education c
Australia and New Zealand

Harmony: from the Oxford Book of Carols by

©Oxford University Press   Martin Sha

525

Because of their irregular metre, the four verses should be
sung by a soloist. Everyone responds in the chorus.

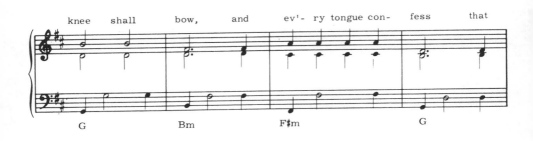

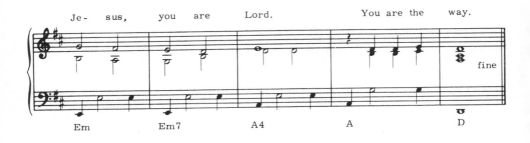

2. I am the Truth.
   And I set my spirit deep within your hearts,
   and you will know me, and love me, ;
   and the truth I give to you will set you free.

3. I am the Life.
   The living waters I pour out for you.
   Anyone who drinks of the waters that I give
   will have eternal life.

4. I am the Word,
   the true light that shines brightly in the dark,
   a light that darkness could not overpower,
   The Word made Flesh, risen among you.

Words: Mary Barrett
(based on St. John)
Music: Mary Barrett and
Eileen Binding

© 1978 Kevin Mayhew Ltd.

526

Response

Keep in mind that Je-sus Christ has died for us and is ri-sen from the

Fine

dead. He is our sa-ving Lord, he is joy for all a - ges.

Repeat the response after each verse, or after verses 2, 4, 6.

Verses 1 and 2

D.C.

1. If we die with the Lord, we shall live with the Lord.
2. If we en - dure with the Lord, we shall reign with the Lord.

Verses 3-6

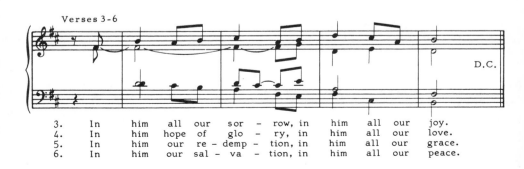

D.C.

3. In him all our sor - row, in him all our joy.
4. In him hope of glo - ry, in him all our love.
5. In him our re - demp - tion, in him all our grace.
6. In him our sal - va - tion, in him all our peace.

S A

Keep in mind that Je-sus Christ has died for us and is ri-sen from the

dead. He is our sa-ving Lord, he is joy for all a – ges.

Words and music: Lucien Deiss

527

Refrain

Laud-a- to sii,   O mi Sig- no- re. Laud-a- to sii,

O mi Sig- no- re. Laud-a- to sii,   O mi Sig- no- re.

Laud-a- to sii,   O mi Sig- no- re.   Last time rit. Laud-a- to sii,

pp   fine

1. Yes, be praised in all your crea-tures, bro-ther sun and sis-ter moon;

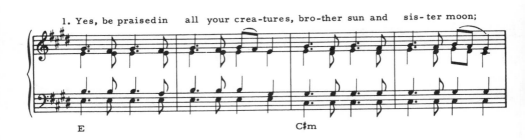

in the stars and in the wind, air and fire and flow- ing wa- ter.

A   B7

D.C.

'Laudato sii, O mi Signore ' means
' Be praised, O my Lord '

2. For our sister, mother earth,
   she who feeds us and sustains us;
   for her fruits, her grass, her flowers,
   for the mountains and the oceans.

3. Praise for those who spread forgiveness,
   those who share your peace with others,
   bearing trials and sickness bravely!
   Even sister death won't harm them.

4. For our life is but a song,
   and the reason for our singing
   is to praise you for the music;
   join the dance of your creation.

5. Praise to you, Father most holy,
   praise and thanks to you, Lord Jesus,
   praise to you, most Holy Spirit,
   life and joy of all creation!

Words, from St Francis of Assisi, by Damian Lundy
Music, of unknown Italian origin, arranged by Michael Irwin

528

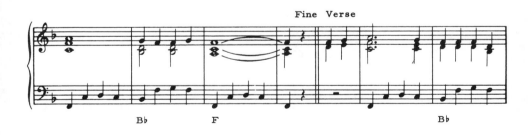

Lay your hands gently upon us,
let their touch render your peace;
let them bring your forgiveness and healing
lay your hands, gently lay your hands.

1. You were sent to free the broken hearted.
   You were sent to give sight to the blind.
   You desire to heal all our illness.
   Lay your hands, gently lay your hands.

2. Lord, we come to you through one another.
   Lord, we come to you in all our need.
   Lord, we come to you seeking wholeness.
   Lay your hands, gently lay your hands.

Words and Music: Carey Landry

529

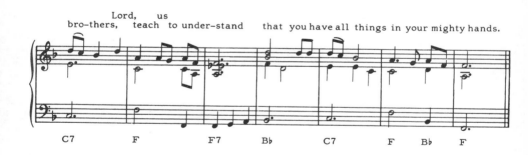

home. Take me and fold me in your loving arms, then I shall be

F   C7   F   F+   B♭   Gm   C

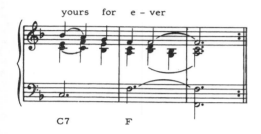

yours for e – ver

C7   F

Words and music: Peter Skinner

© Assigned to Mayhew-McCrimmon Ltd

Harmony: for Celebration Hymnal
by Roger Humphrey

Leave your country and your people,
leave your fam'ly and your friends.
Travel to the land I'll show you;
God will bless the ones he sends.

1. Go like Abraham before you,
when he heard the Father's call,
walking forth in faith and trusting;
God is master of us all.

2. Sometimes God's Word is demanding,
leave security you know,
breaking ties and bonds that hold you,
when the voice of God says: "Go".

3. Take the path into the desert,
barren seems the rock and sand.
God will lead you through the desert
when you follow his command.

4. Go with courage up the mountain,
climb the narrow, rocky ledge,
leave behind all things that hinder,
go with only God as pledge.

Words: from Genesis 12:1 ff
by Willard F. Jabusch
Music: Willard F. Jabusch

© Willard F. Jabusch

Harmony: for Celebration Hymnal
by John Rombaut

© 1981 Mayhew-McCrimmon Ltd

531

Verse
CANTOR

1. Lest he be too far from us, he prepared his com- ing.
2. He is ev- ery- where at hand, ev- ery de- tail hu- man.

p

Alternative accompaniment:-

He who longed to share our fate made with us his dwell- ing.
Yet he is not re- cog-nized, si- lent, ne- ver spo- ken.

Or:-

3. God from God and light from light,
   all creation's keeper,
   has a human face and talks,
   man to man as brother.

4. So with patience as your guide,
   show all kinds of goodness:
   owe each other, for his sake,
   only love and kindness.

5. Now be carefree, full of joy:
   God, whom we do worship,
   brushes past us, day by day,
   shares our home and kinship.

+ ALL

1-5. There a- mong you stands One you do not know.

Or:-

Refrain

R. There a- mong you stands one you do not know.

Or:-

Words: Huub Oosterhuis, translated by Tony Barr
Music: Bernard Huijbers

Music © 1982 by Bernard Huijbers.
Text © Huub Oosterhuis
Translation © 1982 Tony Barr

532

DAS SOLLT IHR (11.11.11.5)

1. Let all who share one bread and cup remember
   the oneness of that host of countless number
   of those who are, as children of one Father,
   part of each other.

2. If only we would live as sisters, brothers,
   put faith to practice, truly care for others,
   then we would do the will of him who sends us,
   whose love attends us.

3. Use for yourself our highest and profoundest,
   so that, O Lord, with all men who surround us,
   we may enjoy a world in Christ united,
   so long awaited.

Words: J.A. Cramer (1723–88)
      translated by Fred Kaan
Music: Johann Cruger (1653)

Words ©1972 Fred Kaan

Harmony: Cantate Domino (4th Edition)

©1980 World Council of Churches

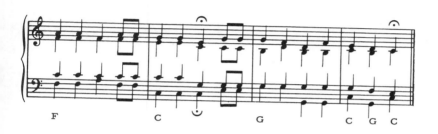

Let it breathe on me, let it
   breathe on me.
Let this breath of God now
   breathe on me.
Let it breathe on me, let it
   breathe on me.
Let this breath of God now
   breathe on me.

Words and music: William E. Booth-Clibborn

©1925, 1949 Renewal by William E. Booth-Clibborn

Harmony: for Celebration Hymnal
   by Eric Welch

©1981 Mayhew-McCrimmon Ltd

534

SOVEREIGN (887.887)

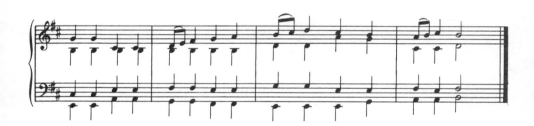

1. Let us praise our sov'reign Saviour,
   Christ, our shepherd, and our leader,
   till the ending of our days.
   Though we praise him all we're able,
   all our praise is all too feeble;
   he is far beyond all praise.

2. He, before he gave to others,
   gave his little band of brothers
   both his body and his blood –
   not a mere symbolic token,
   blood outpoured and body broken –
   as an everlasting food.

3. What a theme to baffle study –
   that mere bread becomes his body,
   wine his blood! The King of kings
   comes down to this altar duly
   to repeat the wonder daily,
   quite outside the run of things.

   Repeat verse 1

(Suggested use:
Verse 1: unison with organ
Verse 2: SATB with organ
Verse 3: SATB a capella
Verse 1: unison with organ)

Words: J. Gordon Nichols
Music: Philip Duffy

LINSTEAD (88.88 and refrain)

535

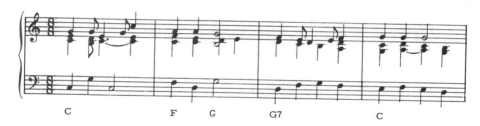

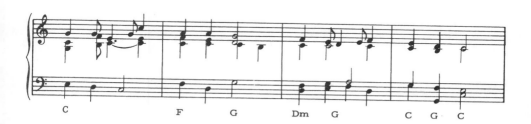

1. Let us talents and tongues employ,
   reaching out with a shout of joy:
   bread is broken, the wine is poured,
   Christ is spoken and seen and heard.

   **Jesus lives again, earth can breathe again,
   pass the Word around: loaves abound!**

2. Christ is able to make us one,
   at his table he sets the tone,
   teaching people to live to bless,
   love in word and in deed express.

3. Jesus calls us in, sends us out
   bearing fruit in a world of doubt,
   gives us love to tell, bread to share:
   God-Immanuel everywhere!

Words: Fred Kaan
Music: Jamaican traditional
adapted by Doreen Potter

536

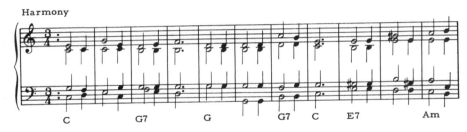

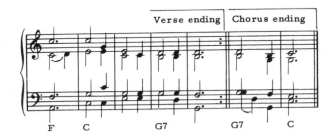

1. Light the Advent candle one.
   Now the waiting has begun,
   we have started on our way:
   time to think of Christmas day.

   **Candle, candle, burning bright,
   shining in the cold winter night.
   Candle, candle, burning bright,
   fill our hearts with Christmas light.**

2. Light the Advent candle two.
   Think of humble shepherds who
   filled with wonder at the sight
   of the child on Christmas night.

3. Light the Advent candle three.
   Think of heav'nly harmony:
   angels singing "Peace on earth"
   at the blessed Saviour's birth.

4. Light the Christmas candles now!
   Sing of donkey, sheep and cow.
   Birthday candles for the King —
   let the "Alleluias" ring!

Words: Mary Lu Walker
Music: Mary Lu Walker

©1975 Missionary Society of St Paul the Apostle
    in the State of New York

Harmony: for Celebration Hymnal
    by Eric Welch

©1981 Mayhew-McCrimmon Ltd

537

1. Like a sea with-out a shore love di-vine is bound-less.

G — C D7 — G — C D7

Time is now and ev-er-more and his love sur-rounds us.

G — C D7 — G — C D7

Chorus
Ma- ra- na- tha! Ma- ra- na- tha!

G — Em — Am D7

Ma- ra- na- tha! Come, Lord Je- sus, come!

G — Em — C D7 G

2. So that mankind could be free
he appeared among us,
Blest are those who have not seen,
yet believe his promise.

3. All our visions, all our dreams,
are but ghostly shadows
of the radiant clarity
waiting at life's close.

4. Death where is your victory?
Death where is your sting?
Closer than the air we breathe
is our risen King.

'Maranatha' is an Aramaic phrase meaning
'Lord, come!' (See 1 Corinthians 16:22)

Words and Music: Estelle White

538

1. Like the deer that thirsts for water,
   O God, I long for you.
   Weeping, I have heard them taunt me:
   'What help is in your God?'

2. Gladly I would lead your people
   rejoicing to your house.
   Trust in God, my soul, and praise him
   and he will dry your tears.

3. Grief and pain, like roaring torrents,
   had swept my soul away.
   But his mercy is my rescue,
   I will praise him all my days.

4. Weeping, I have heard them taunt me:
   'What help is in your God?'
   Rock of Strength, do not forget me;
   in you alone I trust.

(5. To the Father, praise and honour;
   all glory to the Son;
   honour to the Holy Spirit;
   let God be glorified.)

Optional response

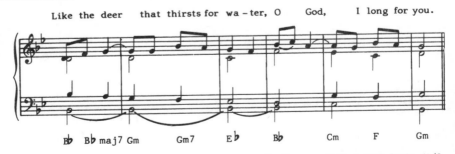

Words: paraphrased from Psalm 41/2
by Luke Connaughton
Music: Kevin Mayhew

1. Look around, look around you
    and you will see,
   all the sunshine, the sky so blue
    and feel the breeze;
   they are saying:
    God's love is real.

2. Take a walk thru' the countryside
    and watch the trees,
   hear the birds singing sweetly
    and you will feel peace
   and joy
    you've never known.

If you doubt your Father loves you,
stop and think for just a while:
is it need or greed that drives you
to be crying all the time?

3. Cleanse your mind, open wide your
                              heart,
    and call to him,
   and he'll fill you with wisdom
    so that you'll begin
   to realise
    God's love is real.

Words and music: Ronald Gokool
Harmony: for Celebration Hymnal
by James O'Donnell

540

With strength and intensity

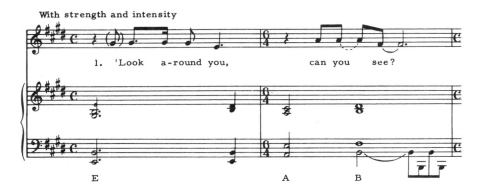

1. 'Look a-round you, can you see?

E   A   B

Times are troubled, peo-ple grieve. See the vio-lence,

E   A   B   E

feel the hardness; all my peo- ple, weep with me.'

Am   B   E

Refrain

Ky- ri- e e- lei- son, Chris- te e-
lei- son, Ky- ri- e e- le-
i- son.

E   A   B   E
A   B   E   A
B   E   E

Final ending

2. 'Walk among them, I'll go with you.
   Reach out to them with my hands.
   Suffer with me, and together
   we will serve them, help them stand. '

3. Forgive us, Father; hear our prayer.
   We would walk with you anywhere,
   through your suff'ring, with forgiveness,
   take your life into the world.

Words and Music: Jodi Page Clark

541

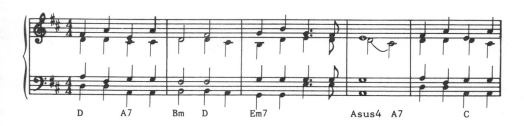

D   A7   Bm   D   Em7   Asus4   A7   C

Bm   Em7   Asus4   A   G   D   Em   D7

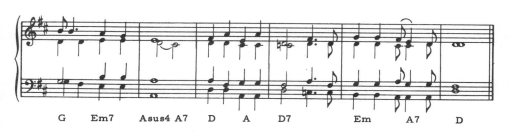

G   Em7   Asus4 A7   D   A   D7   Em   A7   D

1. Looking at the sunrise
   heralding the dawn;
   list'ning to the birds sing
   hearing ev'ry sound.
   I'm at peace with nature,
   because, I suppose,
   all my cares and troubles
   are resting with the Lord.

2. Children playing round me,
   laughter's in my heart.
   People toiling sadly,
   comfort I impart.
   Joy is with me daily
   and it's all I know,
   because Jesus loves me,
   for he told me so.

3. Listen to me, brothers,
   heed to what I say;
   place your trust in Jesus,
   let him guide your way.
   He will not forsake or
   from you turn away;
   peace is yours, my brothers,
   Jesus is the way.

Words and music: Ronald Gokool

Harmony: for Celebration Hymnal
by Eric Welch

Verses 1 - 4 | Verse 5

1. Lord, confronted with your might,
   with your purity and light
   we are made with shame to see
   all that we fail to be.

2. Conscious of our feeble will,
   wanting good, but choosing ill,
   we are sorry for our sin:
   Lord, make us clean within.

3. Steady, Lord, our stumbling feet,
   free our spirits from deceit.
   Give us openness for pride;
   we have no place to hide.

4. Lift us from despair and grief,
   help us in our unbelief.
   As we spread our hands to you,
   fill us with life anew.

5. For the sake of Christ, forgive,
   speak the Word, and we shall live.
   Send us forward on our way,
   Lord, with our heads held high.

Words: Fred Kaan
Music: Doreen Potter

543

REGENT SQUARE (87.87.87)

1. Lord en-throned in heav'n-ly splendour, first be-got-ten from the dead,

thou a-lone, our strong de-fend-er, lift-est up thy peo-ple's head.

Al- le-lu- ia, al- le-lu- ia, Je- sus, true and liv- ing bread!

2.· Prince of life, for us thou livest,
    by thy body souls are healed;
    Prince of peace, thy peace thou givest,
    by thy blood is pardon sealed;
    alleluia, alleluia,
    Word of God, in flesh revealed.

3. Paschal Lamb! Thine offering finished,
    once for all, when thou wast slain,
    in its fullness undiminished
    shall for evermore remain,
    alleluia, alleluia,
    cleansing souls from every stain.

4. Great high priest of our profession,
    through the veil thou enteredst in;
    by thy mighty intercession
    grace and mercy thou canst win:
    alleluia, alleluia,
    only sacrifice for sin.

5. Life-imparting heavenly manna,
    stricken rock, with streaming side,
    heaven and earth, with loud hosanna,
    worship thee, the Lamb who died;
    alleluia, alleluia,
    risen, ascended, glorified!

Words: G.H. Bourne 1840-1925 © Oxford University Press   Music: H. Smart 1813-79

D G D D G D A7

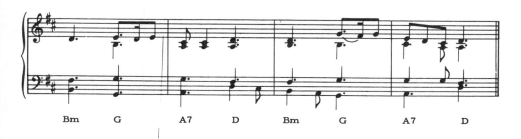

Bm G A7 D Bm G A7 D

1. Lord, graciously hear us,
   hear us as we call on you,
   we tried to be faithful, Lord,
   but we have sinned against you.

2. You gave us your message,
   you showed us the way to live;
   we tried to be faithful, Lord,
   but we have not understood.

3. Lord, show us your mercy,
   heal those we have wounded here;
   we wanted to love like you,
   but we have forgotten the way.

4. Speak, Lord, to your people,
   speak, now, in a million ways;
   we want to be true to you,
   help, Lord, and forgive us, we pray.

Words and Music: Anne Conway

© 1976 Anne Conway

545 CHARLTON (77 77 D)

1. Lord, in ev-ery-thing I do let me al-ways follow you; let the mo-ments of my days ov-er-flow with end-less praise; take my hands and let them move at the im-pulse of your love; ev-ery move that I shall make Lord, di-rect the steps I

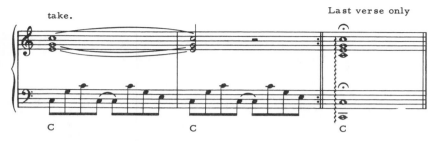

take.

Last verse only

2. Lord, with all your people here
   you invite me to draw near;
   Lord, accept the gifts I bring,
   Lord, accept the praise I sing.
   Take my lips and let them speak
   of your goodness through the week;
   let me echo this refrain
   till I come to you again.

3. As I listen to your call,
   Lord, I want to give my all;
   take my heart and mind and use
   every power you shall choose;
   all I have has come from you
   and I offer back to you
   only what was yours before:
   take my life for evermore.

Choir Accompaniment to verse 2

Words: Patrick Appleford, based on the hymn 'Take my
life' by Francis Havergal 1836-1879
Music: Alan Wilson

© 1979 Josef Weinberger Ltd.

546 HERR JESU CHRIST (88.88)

1. Lord Jesus Christ, be present now,
   and let your Holy Spirit bow
   all hearts in love and truth today
   to hear your Word and keep your way.

2. May your glad tidings always bring
   good news to men that they may sing
   of how you came to save all men.
   Instruct us till you come again.

3. To God the Father and the Son
   and Holy Spirit three in one;
   to you, O blessed Trinity,
   be praise throughout eternity.

Words: author unknown
Music: Cantionale Germanicum
       (Dresden (1681)

1. Lord of Cre - a - tion, to you be all praise!
Most migh - ty your work - ing, most wond- rous your ways.
Your glo - ry and might are be - yond us to tell,
and yet in the heart of the hum - ble you dwell.

2. Lord of all power, I give you my will,
in joyful obedience your tasks to fulfil.
Your bondage is freedom, your service is song,
and, held in your keeping, my weakness is strong.

3. Lord of all wisdom, I give you my mind,
rich truth that surpasses man's knowledge to find.
What eye has not seen and what ear has not heard
is taught by your Spirit and shines from your Word.

4. Lord of all bounty, I give you my heart;
I praise and adore you for all you impart:
your love to inspire me, your counsel to guide,
your presence to cheer me, whatever betide.

5. Lord of all being, I give you my all;
if e'er I disown you I stumble and fall;
but, sworn in glad service your word to obey,
I walk in your freedom to the end of the way.

*This hymn may also
start at verse 2.*

*Words © Mrs J. Tyrell
Music: Irish traditional melody*

548

1. Lord, this paschal time reminds us
   how you came back from the dead.
   Firm and true the faith that binds us
   to our glorious, risen Head.
   Alleluia, alleluia,
   you have risen as you said,
   alleluia, alleluia,
   you have risen as you said.

2. 'Neath the burden of our labour,
   mid our joy and pain and strife,
   in our trying to be neighbour,
   to be parent, husband, wife;
   alleluia, alleluia,
   be to us the source of life,
   alleluia, alleluia,
   be to us the source of life.

3. Make us true to our vocation
   with the strength that comes from you;
   make our life a dedication
   with the love that you imbue.
   Alleluia, alleluia,
   grace and peace in us renew,
   alleluia, alleluia,
   grace and peace in us renew.

4. Hold this vision, Lord, before us;
   in this hope our faith sustain:
   that to life you will restore us
   when at last you come again.
   Alleluia, alleluia,
   make us worthy of your reign,
   alleluia, alleluia,
   make us worthy of your reign.

Words: Denis E. Hurley
Music: Ludwig van Beethoven (1770-1827)

1. Lord, thy word a- bi- deth, and our foot-steps guid- eth;

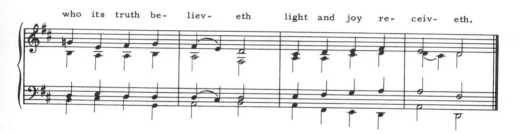

who its truth be- liev- eth light and joy re- ceiv- eth.

2. When our foes are near us,
   then thy word doth cheer us,
   word of consolation,
   message of salvation.

3. When the storms are o'er us,
   and dark clouds before us,
   then its light directeth,
   and our way protecteth.

4. Word of mercy, giving
   courage to the living;
   word of life, supplying
   comfort to the dying!

5. O that we discerning
   its most holy learning,
   Lord, may love and fear thee,
   evermore be near thee.

Words: H. W. Baker 1821-77
Music: Adapted by W. H. Monk (1861) from the melody 'Ave, Hierarchia'
       in M. Weisse's (1480-1534) 'Neu Gesangbuchlein' 1531

550

1. Lord, you have come to the lake - side, see - king
nei - ther wealthy or wise men, you on - ly
ask, Lord, that I should love you.

Chorus

With love you have looked in my eyes, Lord, smi - ling gent - ly

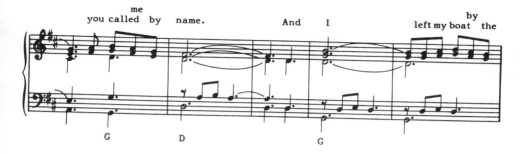

me
you called by name.   And   I   by
left my boat the

G   D   G

lake - side,   now with   you   I will seek o-ther shores.

D   A7   D

2. Lord, you well know that I carry
   in my boat no treasure nor weapon.
   I bring you only
   my willing labour.

3. Lord, you have need of my hands;
   I shall labour that others may rest;
   and from my love, Lord,
   may others love you.

4. Lord, other seas call me onward;
   hope eternal for hearts that are searching;
   and love will bind us
   as friends for ever.

Words and Music: C.Gabarain

© Ediciones Paulinas, Madrid

Translation © Fr.Edmund O'Shea

Arrangement by Stephen Dean

© Mayhew-McCrimmon Ltd

551 GARTAN (67.67)

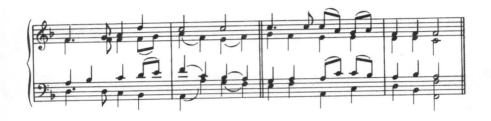

1. Love came down at Christmas,
   love all lovely, love divine;
   love was born at Christmas,
   star and angels gave the sign.

2. Worship we the Godhead,
   love incarnate, love divine;
   worship we our Jesus:
   but wherewith for sacred sign?

3. Love shall be our token,
   love be yours and love be mine,
   love to God and all men,
   love for plea and gift and sign.

Words: Christina Rossetti (1830–1894)
Music: Irish traditional

© Oxford University Press

Refrain

Lu – men Chri – sti, al – le – lu – ia! A – men!

Choir

Verse

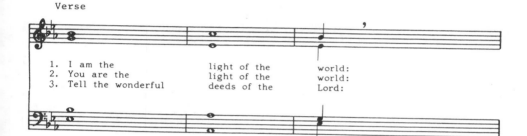

1. I am the light of the world:
2. You are the light of the world:
3. Tell the wonderful deeds of the Lord:

* whoever follows me will never walk in darkness.
* in the same way your light must shine before all!
  he called you from darkness to light.

alternative version:

* he who follows me will not walk in darkness.
* let your light shine before men.

Words: Scripture
Music: Jean-Paul Lecot

553

May the peace of the Lord be with you,
with your friends and your family too.
Let it be, let it grow, and everywhere you go
may the peace of the Lord follow you.

Words and Music: Gary Ault

1. I leave you peace now, it's my peace I give to you:
   not as the world gives do I give to you.

2. Don't be afraid, let your hearts be untroubled:
   have faith in God and have faith in me.

Harmony: for Celebration Hymnal
by Eric Welch

© 1981 Mayhew-McCrimmon Ltd

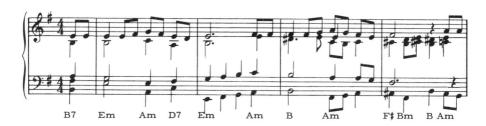

B7   Em   Am   D7   Em   Am   B   Am   F♯ Bm   B Am

F   F7   Am   Bsus4 B7   C   Em   A7   B7   Em

1. Modern man has the city for his home
   where his life is walled in by want and dread,
   pained by nights without sleep and days of grinding work,
   in the struggle to earn his daily bread.

2. In our cities, immense and growing out,
   there are millions from faith and love estranged,
   who need to recapture hope of better things,
   and whose hearts, by the grace of Christ, can change.

3. In the dark of our noisy city life,
   men and women are groping for the light,
   human beings who hunger to see right prevail,
   unaware of the liberating Christ.

4. In the great giant cities of our globe,
   hollowed out by the ways of greed and crime,
   we are set to reflect the likeness of our God
   and to act out renewal's great design.

5. Grow then, cities, to house the world of man,
   with your skyscrapers blotting out the sun.
   Let Christ be the light to shine from human homes
   in the high-rising blocks of steel and stone.

Words: Joao Dias de Araujo
          translated by Fred Kaan
Music: Joao Wilson Faustini

Words ©1972 Fred Kaan
Music ©1967 J.W. Faustini

Harmony: Cantate Domino (4th Edition)

©1980 World Council of Churches

555

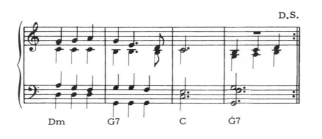

Words and Music: John Glynn
©1978 John Glynn
Harmony: for Celebration Hymnal
by John Rombaut
© 1981 Mayhew McCrimmon Ltd

Mother of Jesus, and mother of lowliness,
bearing the light of the world.
Radiant with glory, the glory of Jesus,
conceived by the Spirit of God.

1. In the beginning of time
God's Holy Spirit did shine,
breathed on the deep and the darkness
    of night,
bringing the promise of light.

2. Then in the fullness of time
came the same Spirit sublime
breathed on the womb of the Virgin
    of grace,
called her the chosen of God.

3. Wond'rous the moment that heard
you say 'Amen' to the Word;
Son of the Father, the Light of
    his light,
face of the Godhead unveiled.

4. Mary, our Lady of light,
you are the Father's delight:
pray for us sinners to Jesus,
    your Son,
show us the light of the world.

Words and music: John Glynn

556

Refrain

Fine   Verse

com - fort me. —————— 1. In this cold, forbid-ding world   where

D   D7

on-ly

man seeks   him-self,   I can find no-one who'll love   or who'll help.—

G   A7   D   D7   G   Em

—— There is on - ly you. ——————

D.C.

A7   D

My God, my God, don't ever desert me,
my God, my God, I need you beside me.
My life is so lonely, my heart is so empty,
my God, only you can comfort me.

1. In this cold, forbidding world
    where man seeks only himself,
    I can find no one who'll love
    or who'll help. There is only you.

2. In my joy I look for laughter,
    in my sorrow I seek a friend;
    but I see only fleeting shadows,
    and then I turn and find you there.

3. None but you know how I'm aching,
    you alone give the solace I seek.
    You alone give me kindness and care
    whenever I despair.

Words and music: Ronald Gokool

Harmony: for Celebration Hymnal
by Roger Humphrey

©1981 Mayhew-McCrimmon Ltd

557

CANTOR

My God, you fa- thom my heart and you know me.

ALL

My God, you fa- thom my heart and you know me.

CANTOR

Noth-ing in me lies con- cealed from your eyes;

ALL

ev-ery thing I do, you al- rea- dy know it. You

Music © Bernard Huijbers
Text © Huub Oosterhuis
Translation © Tony Barr
Published by Jabulani Music Ltd,
9 Patmore Road,
Colchester, Essex.

558

Response

My soul is long-ing for your peace, near to you, my God. Fine

F   Am   Gm   Dm Gm   F

Verse

is   D.C.
Lord, you know that my heart not proud, and my eyes are not lif-ted from the earth.

F   Gm   Am Dm Am   C   Gm

Response for mixed voices

S
A

T
B

2. Lofty thoughts have never filled my mind,
    far beyond my sight all ambitious deeds.

3. In your peace I have maintained my soul,
    I have kept my heart in your quiet peace.

4. As a child rests on his mother's knee,
    so I place my soul in your loving care.

5. Israel, put all your hope in God ,
    place your trust in him, now and evermore.

Words: based on Psalm 130/1
by Lucien Deiss
Music: Lucien Deiss

559

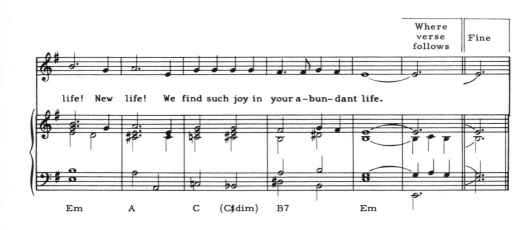

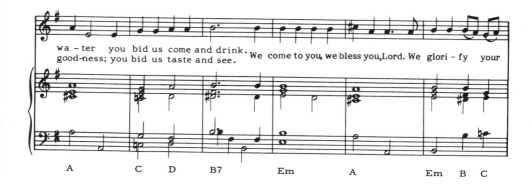

wa – ter   you bid us come and drink. We come to you, we bless you, Lord. We glori – fy   your
good-ness; you bid us taste and see.

A   C   D   B7   Em   A   Em   B   C

name!   We praise you, Lord, we worship you, we thank you for your gift   of new life.

D.C.

B7   Em   A   C (C♯dim) B7   Em

Words and Music: Carey Landry

560

Refrain

No one can give to me that peace / which my ri-sen Lord, my ri-sen King can

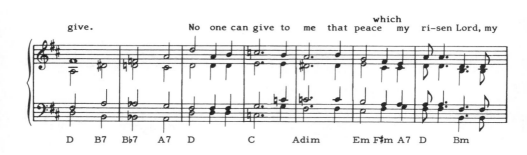

D   C   Adim   Em F♯m A7   D   Bm   G   A7

give.   No one can give to me that peace / which my ri-sen Lord, my

D B7 Bb7 A7 D   C   Adim   Em F♯m A7 D   Bm

Fine   **Verse**

ri-sen King can give.   1. When I look a-round and see all the things / that trou-ble

me and I seem to lose my peace in a world / that's not at ease.   *D.C.*

G   A7   D G D   A7   Em A7   D   A7

D   Bm   E7   A   A7

2. For I take Christ's word as true: "My true peace I give to you,
   but not as the world might give, is my peace that makes you live".

3. His true peace in me will stay, as I live from day to day
   and his joy will never end, and in Heaven it will extend.

4. All the world's in search of peace, but from sin they'll never cease
   how can they expect to find inner joys and peace of mind?

5. All injustice, hate and strife, sins of malice, sex and pride,
   stem from those who've never known, where the seeds of peace were sown.

6. Christ has risen from the dead, triumphed over sin and death
   and he'll never die again, but as Lord he'll live and reign.

561

Verse

1. Now let your peo–ple de–part in peace for we've parta–ken in this your

D   A7

feast. You are the Sa–viour of all the earth, a light to guide us from our

D   A7

Refrain

birth. Ev'–ry time I feel the Spi–rit mo–ving in my heart I will

D   G   D   Em   A7

pray! Ev'–ry time I feel the Spi–rit mo – ving

D   D7   G   D

in my heart   I will pray!

Em   A7   D

2. Sing glory to the Creator Lord,
   and to the Spirit the comforter,
   and unto Jesus the blessed Son,
   forever three and ever one.

Words: from the Nunc Dimittis
       by John C. Ylvisaker
Music: Traditional Spiritual
       arranged by John C. Ylvisaker

©1979 John C. Ylvisaker

Harmony: for Celebration Hymnal
         by John Rombaut

©1981 Mayhew—McCrimmon Ltd

562

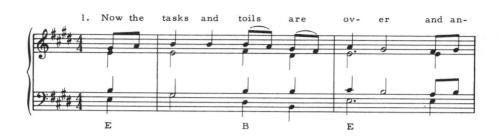

night,   you a- lone will   be   our   re- fuge   and

E   B   C♯m   G♯m

on- ly you our   light.

A   B7   E

2. The moonlight through the branches
   by the evening wind is stirred,
   the stars stand in their places
   as faithful as your word:
   although we shall not hear it,
   though our eyes are held in sleep,
   yet our wakeful hearts turn to you
   their promises to keep.

3. Protect us from all evil,
   from the terrors darkness brings
   that we may rest securely
   in the shadow of your wings.
   O watchful Father, guide us,
   our strength and life restore,
   that we may wake at morning
   to hear your voice once more.

Words and Music: Kevin Nichols, music harmonised by
              Rosalind Pitcher

563

1. Now watch for God's com-ing, be pa-tient till

G   D7   G   D7

then; like sun-shine at noon-time he'll bright-en all

G   D7   G   D7

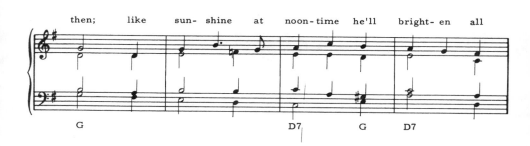

men; who hope in the Lord will pos-sess fer-tile

G   Am   G

land; the poor he will wel-come and grasp in the hand.

D   G   Am   G   Am   D7   G

N. B. The guitar chords should not be used with this harmony.

2. Man's steps are directed, God watches his path;
   he guides him and holds him and saves him from wrath,
   and though he may fall he will not go headlong,
   for God gives sound footing and keeps him from wrong.

3. So wait for his coming, be patient till then;
   the wicked are armed and would kill honest men.
   Their arms shall be broken, no refuge they'll see,
   but saved are the needy by God's own decree.

4. Now those who do evil will wither like grass,
   like green of the springtime they fade and they pass,
   so trust in the Lord and to him give your life,
   he'll bring heart's desires and peace in our strife.

Words: Willard F. Jabusch
Music: Traditional Catalonian Carol,
       arranged by Stephen Dean

564

Em   Am   Bm7 Em   G Em Dsus4 D7 G

Em   Am7 G Am   D   G   C   G   Am7 D/A Em

1. Now with the fading light of day
   Maker of all, to Thee we pray
   that with Thy wonted care and love,
   Thou guard and protect us from above.

2. Take far away each hideous dream,
   things in the night that monstrous seem,
   wiles of our old arch-foe restrain
   lest faltering flesh contract a stain.

3. Father almighty, grace afford,
   grant it through Jesus Christ our Lord,
   who with the Holy Ghost and Thee
   is reigning for all eternity.

Words: Te lucis ante terminum
translated by
Sebastian Bullough
Music: Anthony Milner

D.C.

D

O be joyful in the Lord!
O be joyful in the Lord!
Let us make a joyful noise,
let the whole earth rejoice!
O be joyful in the Lord, all ye lands!

1. Know that the Lord he is God;
   he has made us, we are his.
   We are the sheep of his pasture,
   the people of his hand.

2. Enter his gates with thanksgiving:
   come into his courts with praise.
   Be thankful unto him,
   and speak good of his name.

3. Know that the Lord, he is good:
   his love lasts for ever.
   He's faithful and true
   through ev'ry generation.

Words: Psalm 100
           paraphrased by Jonathan Asprey
Music: Jonathan Asprey

11 11.11 11

1. O comfort my people and calm all their

fear and tell them the time of salvation draws

near. O tell them I come to remove all their

shame, then they will for ever give praise to my name.

2. Proclaim to the cities of Juda my word:
   that gentle yet strong is the hand of the Lord.
   I rescue the captives my people defend
   and bring them to justice and joy without end.

3. All mountains and hills shall become as a plain
   for vanished are mourning and hunger and pain.
   And never again shall these war against you.
   Behold I come quickly to make all things new.

Words: Isaiah 40, paraphrased by Chrysogonus Waddell
Music: Traditional Irish, harmonised by Stephen Dean

567

EISENACH (88.88)

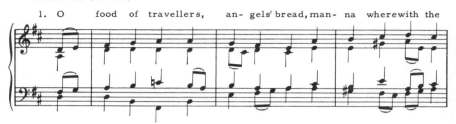

2. O fount of love, O well unpriced,
   outpouring from the heart of Christ,
   give us to drink of very thee,
   and all we pray shall answered be.

3. O Jesus Christ, we pray to thee
   that this thy presence which we see,
   though now in form of bread concealed,
   to us may be in heaven revealed.

Words: Maintzisch Gesangbuch 1661, translated
      by Walter H. Shewring and others
Music: Melody by J.H.Schein 1586-1630,
      harmony by J.S. Bach 1685-1750

O la- dy, full of God's own grace, whose caring hands the child em-

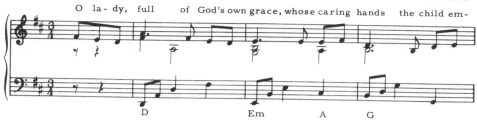

D   Em   A   G

braced, who listened to the Spi-rit's word, believed and trus- ted in the

D   Em   A   G

Chorus

Lord. O vir-gin fair, star of the sea, my dearest moth- er, pray for

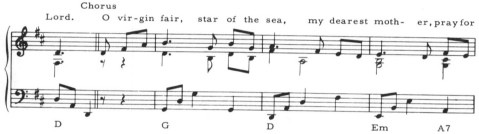

D   G   D   Em   A7

me. O virgin fair, star of the sea, my dearest moth-er, pray for me.

D   G   D   Em   A7   D

2. O lady, who felt daily joy
   in caring for the holy boy,
   whose home was plain and shorn of wealth,
   yet was enriched by God's own breath.

3. O lady, who bore living's pain
   but still believed that love would reign,
   who on a hill watched Jesus die
   as on the cross they raised him high.

4. O lady, who, on Easter day,
   had all your sorrow wiped away
   as God the Father's will was done
   when from death's hold he freed your Son.

Words and Music: Estelle White

569 PASSION CHORALE (76.76.D)

1.   O light forever dawning beyond the darkest night;
O comfort of the mourning, our strength and our delight;
receive our humble pleading for those whose course is run,
lest pardon they be needing for any evil done.

2.   To him who like the eagle arose on conqu'ring wing,
the cross his banner regal, O death, where is your sting?
There's surely no rejection for those who share his strife,
but hope and resurrection and everlasting life.

Words: Denis E. Hurley

© Archdiocese of Durban, South Africa

Music: H.L. Hassler (1564-1612)
         arranged by J.S. Bach

(1685-1750)

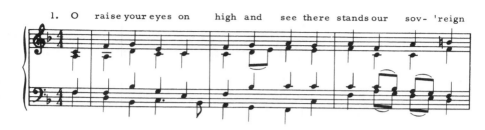

1. O raise your eyes on high and see there stands our sov- 'reign

Lord, his glo-ry is this day revealed, his word a two-edged sword.

2. We glimpse the splendour and the power
   of him who conquered death,
   The Christ in whom the universe
   knows God's creating breath.

3. Of every creed and nation King
   in him all strife is stilled;
   the promise made to Abraham
   in him has been fulfilled.

4. The prophets stand and with great joy
   give witness as they gaze;
   the Father with a sign has sealed
   our trust, our hope, our praise.

5. This glory that today our eyes
   have glimpsed of God's own Son
   will help us ever sing with love
   of Three who are but One.

Words: Ralph Wright
Music: attributed to Jeremiah Clarke,
        c.1659-1707

571

Refrain

O what a gift what a won-der-ful gift; who can

Bm   A   Bm

tell the won-ders of the Lord? Let us o - pen our eyes, our

Em   Bm   F#7   Bm   A

ears, and our hearts; it is Christ the Lord, it is he!   1. In the

Fine.

Bm   A   Bm

stillness of the night, when the world was a-sleep the Lord made his mes-sage

Bm   A   G   A

known.   It was then that his word came down from on high from the

Bm   A

Fa-ther's ro-yal throne: Christ our Lord and our King!

D.C.

G   F#m   Bm   F#m   Bm

2. His mighty Word cuts quick and clean,
   far sharper than a two-edged sword:
   open your eyes, your ears, and your hearts,
   and hear the Word of the Lord:
   Christ our Lord and our King!

3. He came to his people, the chosen race,
   that his Father's will would be known;
   Lion of Judah, Light of the World,
   our Redeemer came to his own;
   Christ our Lord and our King!

4. He lived here among us, he worked here among us,
   morning, night, and day;
   showed us his glory, gave us a promise,
   and then we turned away:
   Christ our Lord and our King!

5. At the Passover meal on the night before he died,
   he lifted up his eyes and prayed.
   The he broke the bread, then he shared the wine –
   the gift that God had made:
   Christ our Lord and our King!

6. On the hill of Calvary, the world held its breath;
   and there for the world to see,
   the Father gave his Son, his very own Son
   for the love of you and me:
   Christ our Lord and our King!

7. Early on that morning when the guards were asleep,
   the Father revealed his might;
   Christ in his glory arose from the dead,
   the Lord of Life and Light:
   Christ our Lord and our King!

8. On the road to Emmaus, the glory that is his,
   the disciples could never see.
   Then he broke the bread, then he shared the wine;
   it is the Lord, it is he:
   Christ our Lord and our King!

9. Now look around you and open your eyes;
   remember the Spirit is here.
   Here within his Church, his people are one.
   Look, the Lord is near;
   Christ our Lord and our King!

Words: Pat Uhl and Michael
        Gilligan
Music: Pat Uhl

© 1967, 1970 The American
Catholic Press

Harmony: for Celebration
Hymnal by Rosalind Pitcher

© 1981 Mayhew—McCrimmon Ltd

572

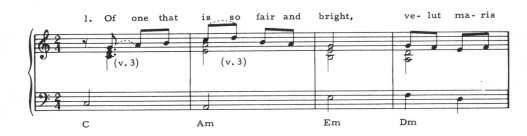

1. Of one that is so fair and bright, ve- lut ma- ris

C   Am   Em   Dm

(v. 3)   (v. 3)

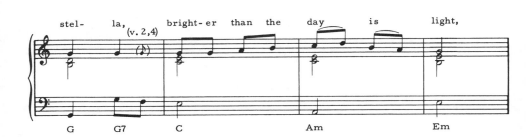

stel- la, (v. 2,4) bright-er than the day is light,

G   G7   C   Am   Em

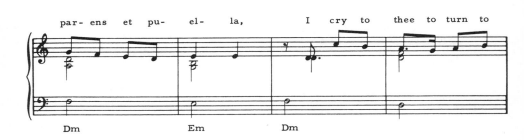

par- ens et pu- el- la, I cry to thee to turn to

Dm   Em   Dm

me: (v. 3) La- dy, pray thy Son for me, tam pi- a,

Em   Dm   Em

that   I   may   *come   to   thee, Ma-   ri-   a.

(v. 4)

Dm   G7   C

* in v. 3 these three quavers carry separate syllables

2. In sorrow, counsel thou art best,
   felix fecundata:
   for all the weary thou art rest,
   mater honorata:
   beseech him in thy mildest mood,
   who for us did shed his blood
   in cruce,
   that we may come to him
   in luce.

3. All this world was forlorn,
   Eva peccatrice,
   till our Saviour Lord was born
   de te genetrice;
   with thy ave sin went away,
   dark night went and in came day
   salutis.
   The well of healing sprang from thee,
   virtutis.

4. Lady, flower of everything,
   rosa sine spina,
   thou borest Jesus, heaven's king,
   gratia divina.
   Of all I say thou bore the prize,
   lady, queen of paradise,
   electa;
   maiden mild, mother
   es effecta.

Words: Anonymous, Medieval
Music: Estelle White

1. Of the Fa- ther's love be- got- ten, ere the

worlds be- gan to be, he is Al- pha and O-

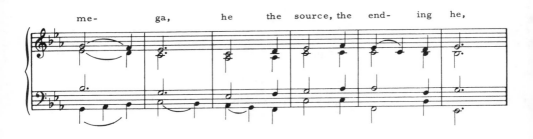

me- ga, he the source, the end- ing he,

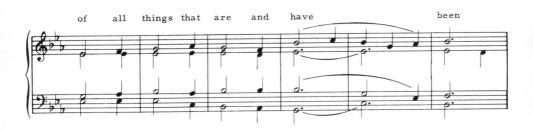

of all things that are and have been

and that fu- ture years shall see: Ev- er- more and

ev- er- more.

2. By his word was all created;
   he commanded, it was done:
   heaven and earth and depth of ocean,
   universe of three in one,
   all that grows beneath the shining
   of the light of moon and sun:
       Evermore and evermore.

3. Blessed was the day for ever
   when the Virgin, full of grace,
   by the Holy Ghost conceiving,
   bore the Saviour of our race,
   and the child, the world's Redeemer,
   first revealed his sacred face:

4. O, ye heights of heaven, adore him,
   angels and archangels sing!
   Every creature bow before him
   singing praise to God our King;
   let no earthly tongue be silent,
   all the world with homage ring:

5. He, by prophets sung, is here now,
   promised since the world began,
   now on earth in flesh descended
   to atone for sins of man.
   All creation praise its Master,
   see fulfillment of his plan:

6. Glory be to God the Father,
   glory be to God the Son,
   glory to the Holy Spirit,
   Persons three, yet Godhead one.
   Glory be from all creation
   while eternal ages run:

Words: Aurelius C. Prudentius 348-c. 413,
       translated by J. M. Neale 1818-66,
       H. W. Baker 1821-77 and others.
Music: 13th century plainchant melody
       adapted by Theodoricus Petrus of
       Nyland in Piae Cantiones, Griefswald 1582.
       Harmony by Redmund Shaw

Harmony © Paul Inwood

574

The chorus is sung by the leader and repeated by all at the beginning, and after each verse. The leader sings the verses alone. The final chorus ends on D - all the others ending on F♯.

Chorus
Oh the word of my Lord, deep with-in my

be-ing, oh the word of my Lord,

you have filled my mind. 1. Be-

fore I formed you in the womb I knew you through and

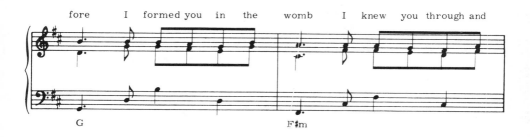

through, I chose you to be mine. Be - fore you left your mother's

Em   A7   D   D7   G

side   I called to   you, my   child,   to   be   my   sign.

D.C.

F#m   Em   Em7   A7

2. I know that you are very young,
   but I will make you strong
   -I'll fill you with my word;
   and you will travel through the land,
   fulfilling my command
   which you have heard.

3. And ev'rywhere you are to go
   my hand will follow you;
   you will not be alone.
   In all the danger that you fear
   you'll find me very near,
   your words my own.

4. With all my strength you will be filled:
   you will destroy and build,
   for that is my design.
   You will create and overthrow,
   reap harvests I will sow
   -your word is mine.

Words (Jeremiah 1) and Music: Damian Lundy

575

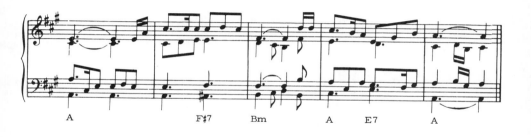

1. On a hill far away stood an old rugged cross,
   the emblem of suff'ring and shame;
   and I loved that old cross where the dearest and best
   for a world of lost sinners was slain.

   So I'll cherish the old rugged cross
   'till my trophies at last I lay down;
   I will cling to the old rugged cross
   and exchange it someday for a crown.

2. Oh that old rugged cross, so despised by the world,
   has a wondrous attraction for me:
   for the dear Lamb of God left his glory above
   to bear it to dark Calvary.

3. In the old rugged cross, stained with blood so divine,
   a wondrous beauty I see.
   For 'twas on that old cross Jesus suffered and died
   to pardon and sanctify me.

4. To the old rugged cross I will ever be true,
   its shame and reproach gladly bear.
   Then he'll call me some day to my home far away
   there his glory for ever I'll share.

Words and music: George Bennar

576

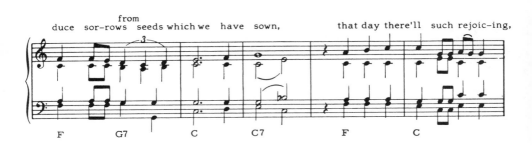

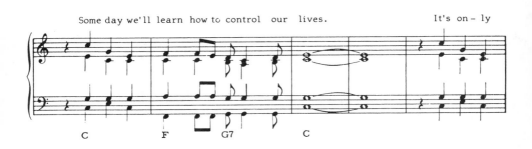

pow'r – ful Lord;   with ra – diant gowns he'll a – dorn us.

C   C7   F   C/G

true
'My children,' he'll say,   one day when love tea–ches us how to

G7/D   C   A7   Dm7   G7

pray.   One day when love tea–ches us how to pray.

C   C♯dim   Dm7   G7   C

One day when love tea–ches us how to pray.

Fm6   G7   A♭   Cmaj7

Words and Music: Ronald Gokool

Harmony: for Celebration Hymnal
by Eric Welch

PASSION CHORALE (76.76.D)

1. Our Father, we have wandered
   and hidden from your face;
   in foolishness have squandered
   your legacy of grace.
   But now in exile dwelling,
   we rise with fear and shame,
   as distant but compelling,
   we hear you call our name.

2. And now at length discerning
   the evil that we do,
   behold us Lord returning
   with hope and trust to you.
   In haste you come to meet us
   and home rejoicing bring,
   in gladness there to greet us
   with calf and robe and ring.

3. O Lord of all the living,
   both banished and restored,
   compassionate, forgiving
   and ever caring Lord,
   grant now that our transgressing,
   our faithlessness may cease.
   Stretch out your hand in blessing
   in pardon and in peace.

Words: Kevin Nichols
c 1974 ICEL Inc
Music: J.S. Bach

577

SECOND TUNE

NESHANIC 7.6.7.6D

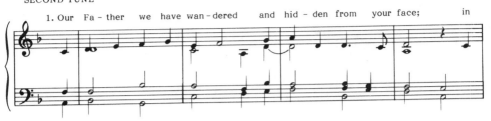

1. Our Father we have wandered and hidden from your face; in

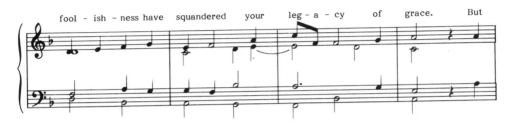

foolishness have squandered your legacy of grace. But

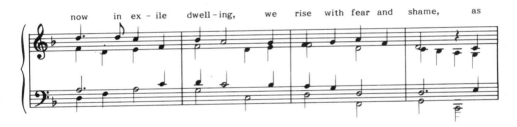

now in exile dwelling, we rise with fear and shame, as

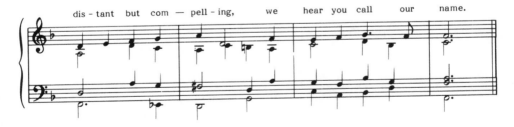

distant but compelling, we hear you call our name.

2. And now at length discerning
the evil that we do,
behold us Lord returning
with hope and trust to you.
In haste you come to meet us
and home rejoicing bring,
in gladness there to greet us
with calf and robe and ring.

3. O Lord of all the living,
both banished and restored,
compassionate, forgiving
and ever caring Lord,
grant now that our transgressing,
our faithlessness may cease.
Stretch out your hand in blessing
in pardon and in peace.

Words: Kevin Nichols
Music: Erik Routley
c 1980 ICEL Inc.

578

Verses
CANTOR

1. He calls my life from out of the grave, he fills my days with

2. This God of ours does not con- demn us, ne- ver re- pays us

3. As a- ny man shows mer- cy to his sons, he is a most mer- ci- ful

CHOIR

Our

1. hap- pi- ness, and like an ea- gle my youth is re- stored. (Respon

2. e- vil for e- vil for he is great- er than our sins. (Respons

3. fa- ther to us. He knows us through for he made us. (Antiphon)

After verse 3, dal 𝄋

help is the name of the Lord and his faith- ful- ness

has no end. Our help is the name of the Lord

To verses 2 & 3

and his faith- ful- ness has no end.

The sequence of this psalm is as follows:-

Antiphon
Verse 1 - Response
Verse 2 - Response
Verse 3 - Antiphon

Words: Versified by Huub Oosterhuis, from Psalm 102 (103): 3-5, 8-10, 13-14.
   Antiphon based on Psalm 120 (121): 2. Translated by Tony Barr.
Music: Bernard Huijbers

579

Slowly

1. Our Sa- viour Je- sus Christ pro- claimed that when we ga- ther in his name he would be there to love and guide, lead us to- wards the Fa- ther's side.

Chorus

Our hearts are long- ing for you, Lord, give us the faith to trust your word.

2. He told us, 'Ask, you will receive,
   seek and you'll find if you believe.
   Knock at the door of love and truth
   and we shall open it for you.'

Chorus

3. His hands brought healing to the blind,
   his words brought ease to troubled minds.
   He said his friends could do the same
   by invocation of his name.

Chorus

4. He came to earth in form of man
   to give to us his Father's plan.
   We are the branches, he the vine,
   we too can share his life divine.

Chorus

ds and Music: Estelle White

© Mayhew–McCrimmon Ltd

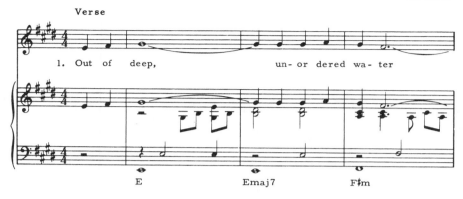

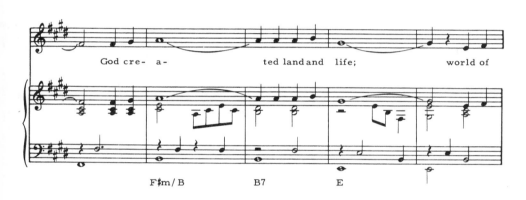

Verse

1. Out of deep, un- or dered wa- ter

E   Emaj7   F#m

God cre- a- ted land and life; world of

F#m/ B   B7   E

bird and beast and la- ter twosome peo-

Emaj7   F#m   F#m/ B

ple, man and wife. There is wa- ter in the

B7   E   G#m

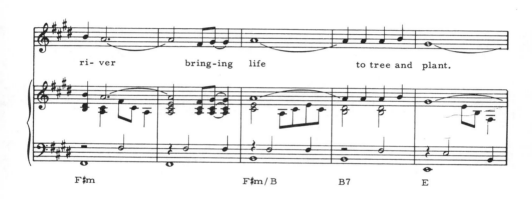

ri- ver bring-ing life to tree and plant.

F#m   F#m/B   B7   E

Let cre- a- tion praise its gi- ver: there is

G#m   F#m

wa - ter in the font.

F#m/B   B7   E

1. Out of deep unordered water
 God created land and life;
 world of beast and bird and later
 twosome people, man and wife.

 There is water in the river
 bringing life to tree and plant.
 Let creation praise its giver:
 there is water in the font.

2. Water on the human forehead,
 birthmark of the love of God,
 is the sign of death and rising,
 through the sea there runs a road.

3. Standing round the font reminds us
 of the Hebrew's climb ashore.
 Life is hallowed by the knowledge
 God has been this way before.

Words: Fred Kaan
Music: Ron Klusmeier

Words © 1968 Stainer & Bell Ltd
Music © 1977 Harmuse Publications

Arrangement © Mayhew-McCrimmon Ltd

581

"Peace is my parting gift to you,
my own peace.
Peace is my parting gift to you,"
says the Lord.   (Jn.14:27)

1. Set your troubled hearts at rest,
   and banish all your fears, for ... (Jn.14:27)

2. I will give you peace such as the world,
   it cannot give, for ... (Jn.14:27)

3. Come to me all who are weary
   and in need of rest, for ... (Mk.11:28)

4. You will find my yoke is easy,
   and my burden light, for ... (Mk.11:30)

5. As the Father sent me, so now
   I am sending you, for ... (Jn.20:21)

6. In my Spirit's power
   all your sins will be forgiven, for ... (Jn.20:22-23)

7. Go and take my gift of peace
   to all throughout the world, for ... (Mk.16:15 & Mt.28:18)

Words: paraphrased from Scripture
by Sister Gabriel (verse 1 and respor
and Robert B. Kelly (verses 2-7)
Music: Sister Gabriel
© 1980 Mayhew-McCrimmon Ltd

1. Peace, perfect peace, in this dark world of sin?
   The blood of Jesus whispers peace within.

2. Peace, perfect peace, by thronging duties pressed?
   To do the will of Jesus, this is rest.

3. Peace, perfect peace, with sorrows surging round?
   On Jesus' bosom nought but calm is found.

4. Peace, perfect peace, with loved ones far away?
   In Jesus' keeping we are safe, and they.

5. Peace, perfect peace, our future all unknown?
   Jesus we know, and he is on the throne.

6. Peace, perfect peace, death shadowing us and ours?
   Jesus has vanquished death and all its powers.

7. It is enough; earth's troubles soon shall cease,
   and Jesus call us to heaven's perfect peace.

Words: E.H. Bickersteth (1823-1906)
Music: Orlando Gibbons (1583-1625)

583

C   G   C   F   G

D.C.

C   F   C   F   C   G7   C

Verse 2

C   G7   C   C   F   G7

Peacetime, peacetime,
time for making peace.
Peacetime, peacetime,
time to say I forgive you,
time for saying 'I love you',
time to live as friends.

1. Happy are they who are makers of peace;
   happy are they who forgive;
   happy are they who know how to love;
   they're the sons and daughters of God.

2. Happy are they who are gentle of heart;
   happy are those who care;
   happy are they who seek the good of all;
   they're the ones so close to God's heart.

Words & Music: Carey Landry

Harmony: G.B.Brown & D.M.Herbert

Copyright © 1973 Carey Landry and North
American Liturgy Resources, 10802 N.23rd
Ave., Phoenix, AZ 85029, U.S.A.
All rights reserved. Used with permission.

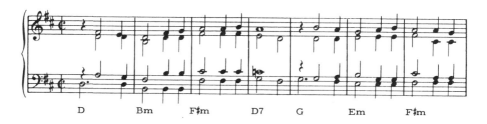

D   Bm   F♯m   D7   G   Em   F♯m

Bm   Em   A7   D   F♯m   Bm B♭dim D   A7   D

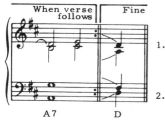

When verse follows | Fine

A7   D

1. Praise the Lord for the Heavens above!
   Praise the Lord for the sun and the moon!
   Praise the Lord for the stars shining bright!
   Yes praise, O praise the Lord!

2. Praise the Lord for the breezes and the winds!
   Praise the Lord for the cold and heat!
   Praise the Lord for the showers so cool!
   Yes praise, O praise the Lord!

3. Praise the Lord for the nights and the days!
   Praise the Lord for the weeks and the months!
   Praise the Lord for the years as they pass!
   Yes praise, O praise the Lord!

4. Praise the Lord for redemption from sin!
   Praise the Lord for salvation is ours!
   Praise the Lord for that glorious day!
   Yes praise, O praise the Lord!

5. Praise the Lord for his passion and death!
   Praise the Lord for his sufferings so cruel!
   Praise the Lord for arising from death!
   Yes praise, O praise the Lord!

To give variety, this may be sung

- in unison
- in two parts – follow Soprano and Alto
- in three parts – follow Soprano, Alto and Tenor
- in four parts – SATB

Words and music: Douglas Rowe SJ

©1980 Mayhew-McCrimmon Ltd

Harmony: for Celebration Hymnal
by John Rombaut

©1981 Mayhew-McCrimmon Ltd

585

AUSTRIA (87.87 D)

1. Praise the Lord! Ye heav'ns a-dore him; praise him, an-gels,

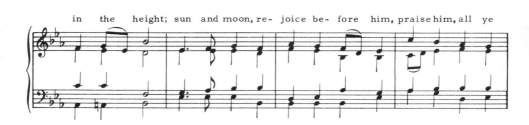

in the height; sun and moon, re- joice be- fore him, praise him, all ye

stars and light.   Praise the Lord! For he hath spo- ken;

worlds his migh- ty voice o-beyed: Laws, which nev- er

shall   be   bro-   ken,   for   their   guid-   ance   he   hath   made.

2. Praise the Lord! for he is glorious;
   never shall his promise fail:
   God hath made his saints victorious;
   sin and death shall not prevail.
   Praise the God of our salvation;
   hosts on high, his power proclaim;
   heaven and earth and all creation,
   laud and magnify his name!

3. Worship, honour, glory, blessing,
   Lord, we offer to thy name;
   young and old, thy praise expressing,
   join their Saviour to proclaim.
   As the saints in heaven adore thee,
   we would bow before thy throne;
   as thine angels serve before thee,
   so on earth thy will be done.

Words: Verses 1-2 from the Foundling Hospital Collection 1796
        Verse 3 by E. Osler 1798-1863
Music: Croatian folk tune, adaptation attributed to F.J.Haydn 1732-1809

586

Refrain — Fine — Verse

Gm   Dm   Gm   Gm   Cm

D.C.

Gm   Cm   Gm   F   Cm   Dm7

Praise to the Lord! Praise him!
Praise to the Lord!

1. Shout to God, all you heavens,
   and clap your hands you on earth.
   Enter into his presence
   exulting and singing for joy!

2. Know that God is our Father;
   he made us, we are his own.
   Come to him with thanksgiving
   extolling and blessing his name.

3. Merciful to us, sinners,
   compassionate to his sons,
   he has sent his beloved
   to guide us in justice and peace!

4. Praise him, then, with full voices
   and sing to him from the heart!
   Gather, Christians, together,
   together, to joyfully sing.

5. Praise the Lord with trumpet.
   O praise his name with the dance;
   celebrate with the cymbal,
   exalt him with drum, pipe and string!

Words (adapted from Psalms)
and music: Paschal Jordan
Harmony: for Celebration Hymnal
by Eric Welch

Refrain

Rain down jus-tice you heavens from a-bove; let the earth bring forth for us

Em   A   C D Em   Bm   Am

To verses

(v.4)

the one who is to come.

Em   C   D   Bm   A   Em   A   Em

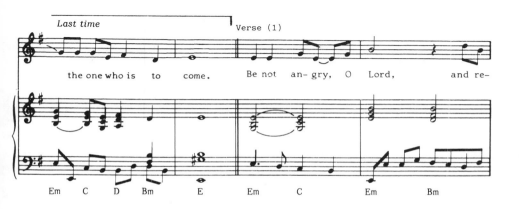

Last time   Verse (1)

the one who is to come.   Be not an-gry, O Lord, and re-

Em   C   D   Bm   E   Em   C   Em   Bm

mem–ber no lon–ger our sin–ful–ness. Our ci–ty, the ci–ty of your

A   C   Bm   Em   Am   D

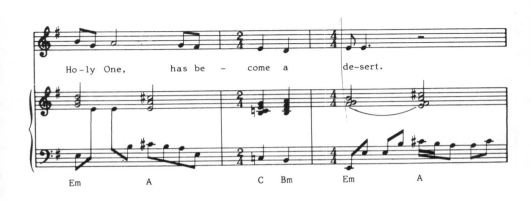

Ho–ly One, has be – come a de–sert.

Em   A   C Bm   Em   A

Si – on is ly–ing in ru–ins; Je–ru–sa–lem, hav–ing fallen lies

Bm7   C   Am   D   Em   Bm

slaved   us   the   day   he   takes   a – way   the   yoke   of   our   cap –

ti – vi – ty.

4. Be com – for – ted, be com – for – ted my peo – ple,   your sal –

va – tion   is   ve – ry   close   at   hand.   Why   are   your   hearts   so   full   of

sor   –   row,   why   does   such   grief   so   es – trange you?

Do   not   be   a – fraid   any   more   I   am   the

Promised   One,   the   hope   of   the   ages.   You   are   my

peo – ple   and   soon   I   come   to   res – cue   you;   I   am   the

Ho – ly   One,   the   Lord   your   Re – dee – mer.

Words: based on the Rorate Caeli by Tony Barr
Music: Tony Barr

© 1967, 1979 Tony Barr

588

F♯m   B   E   C♯m   F♯m   B

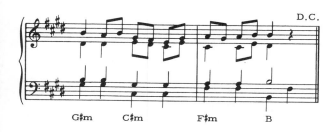

D.C.

G♯m   C♯m   F♯m   B

Rejoice, and shout for joy
sing out in praise for what the Lord has done.
It's right to praise him and sing a new song.
Play it loudly. Sing so joyfully.
For his love it fills the earth.

1. O the words of the Lord are true
and his works are worthy of trust.
He loves what we do that's righteous
and what we do that's just.
He merely spoke and the world began
the heav'ns were formed with moons and stars.
He made the oceans by pouring them
into vast reservoirs.

2. With one breath he can scatter
the plans of a whole nation.
His intentions are the same
for ev'ry generation.
Happy is the nation whose God is the Lord.
Not the king whose army can boast a powerful sword.

3. O the Lord looks down from heaven
and he knows ev'ry thing we do.
He watches over those who obey him
and trust in his love so true.
O the Lord he saves and helps us
and protects us like a shield.
We depend on him. He is our hope.
To him alone we yield.

Words: based on Psalm 33
by Anne Seymour
Music: Anne Seymour

© 1979 Anne Seymour

Harmony: for Celebration Hymnal
by John Rombaut

© 1981 Mayhew-McCrimmon Ltd

589

Rejoice, rejoice, rejoice!
Come, let us praise the Lord!
Rejoice, rejoice, rejoice!
Come, let us bless his name!
Rejoice, rejoice, rejoice!
Come, let us praise the Lord!
Praise the Lord! Praise the Lord!
　　Praise the Lord!

1. Holy, holy, holy!
    Holy, holy, holy!
    Holy, holy, holy!
    O, holy is the Lord!

2. Glory, glory, glory!
    Glory, glory, glory!
    Glory, glory, glory!
    O, glory to the Lord!

Words and music: Norbert Farrell

Harmony: for Celebration Hymnal
　　　　　by Eric Welch

© 1981 Mayhew—McCrimmon Ltd

590

Verses 1-3 Cantor (Verse 4 All, Unison)

Remember man, that you are dust, and un-to

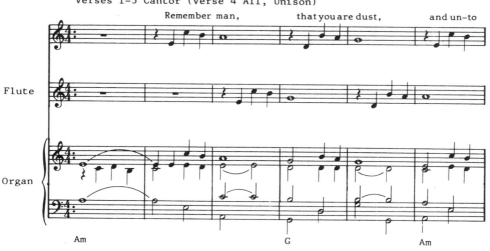

Flute

Organ

Am   G   Am

dust   you shall re-turn.   Refrain All

O who are we,   mere creature

Flute

Organ

G   C   G   Em

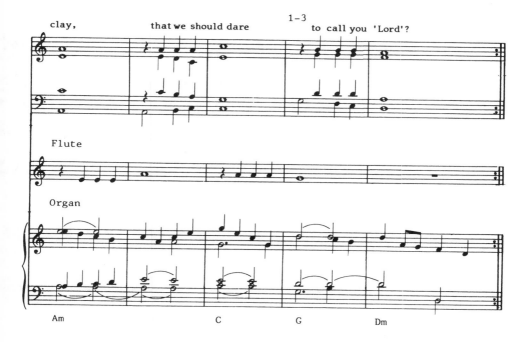

clay, that we should dare 1–3 to call you 'Lord'?

Flute

Organ

Am   C   G   Dm

4 CODA what hope you bring.

Flute

Organ

G   Dm Em   A

2. "Fear not, my child, I am your God.
For you I came; for you I died."
What gift is this – a creature God!
– And in return, what can we give?

3. "O lift your heart, your heart of stone:
no longer lost, you are my own."
O, we have sinned, deserve to die:
how can our pride admit your love?

4. O Lord of love, we turn to you:
forgive, and heal, and make us new.
No eye can see, no ear can hear,
no mind conceive what hope you bring,
what hope you bring.

Words and music: John Glynn

591

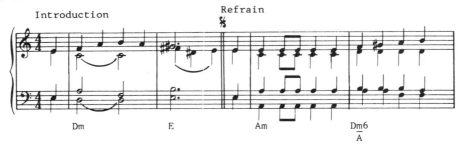

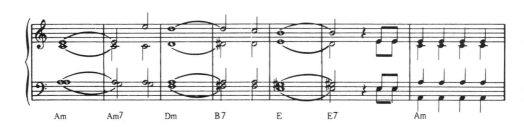

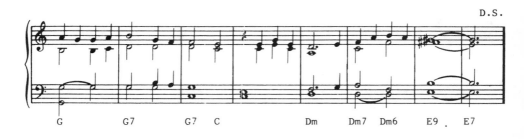

Return to the Lord, return, O Israel!
He calls to you.
For the Lord is full of love and tender mercy;
he waits for your heart.

1. What shall I do with you, O my people?
    This love of yours so quickly disappears. (Hosea 6:4)

2. When will you share your bread with the hungry?
    When will you welcome in the homeless poor? (Isaiah 58:7)

3. I do not take delight in burnt off'ring.
    Give me yourself, your crushed and broken heart. (Psalm 51:17)

4. And I will plant my law deep within you.
    Deep in your heart will I inscribe my name. (Jeremiah 31:31)

5. I love you with a love everlasting;
    I hold you constantly close to my heart. (Jeremiah 31:31)

Words: Scripture
Music: Paschal Jordan

Harmony: for Celebration Hymnal
        by Eric Welch

592 PETRA (77.77 77)

1. Rock of a-ges, cleft for me, let me hide myself in thee;

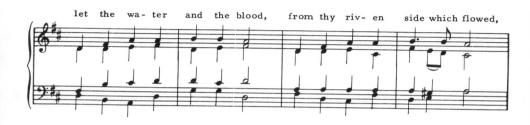

let the wa-ter and the blood, from thy riv-en side which flowed,

be of sin the doub-le cure: cleanse me from its guilt and power.

2. Not the labours of my hands
   can fulfil thy law's demands;
   could my zeal no respite know,
   could my tears for ever flow,
   All for sin could not atone:
   thou must save, and thou alone.

3. Nothing in my hand I bring,
   simply to thy cross I cling;
   naked, come to thee for dress;
   helpless, look to thee for grace;
   foul, I to the fountain fly;
   wash me, Saviour, or I die.

4. While I draw this fleeting breath,
   when my eyelids close in death,
   when I soar through tracts unknown,
   see thee on thy judgement throne;
   rock of ages, cleft for me,
   let me hide myself in thee.

Words: A. M. Toplady, 1740-78
Music: R. Redhead, 1820-1901

This may be sung as a round.

2. Ask and it shall be given unto you,
   seek and ye shall find;
   knock, and it shall be opened unto you;
   allelu, alleluia.

This second verse is not part of the song as
originally written. The origin is unknown.

Words and Music: Karen Lafferty

© 1972 Maranatha! Music, California.

1. Send forth your Spirit, God our Father,
    as you have sent him in the past:
    at Gabriel's word, by Jordan's water,
    as Jesus went to pray and fast.

2. In this same Spirit he proclaimed you
    on Juda's hills, by Galilee,
    he called us to your heav'nly kingdom,
    he died and rose triumphantly.

3. And now though seen by us no longer
    he rests not from the task begun,
    but breathes the Spirit of his sonship
    on men of ev'ry race and tongue.

4. May he be with us at this moment
    and give us of your Spirit still,
    that we may do the work that waits us
    and strive your purpose to fulfil.

At confirmation

5. May all who come for confirmation
    be richly with your Spirit sealed:
    to love and serve you in their brothers,
    until your glory is revealed.

Words: Denis E. Hurley

© Archdiocese of Durban, South Africa

Music: Clement C. Scholefield (1839–1904)

595

Send forth your Spirit, O Lord.
Send forth your Spirit on these your chosen ones.
Send forth your Spirit of love.

1. To show the love of the Father,
   to show the love of the Son.
   To show the love of Jesus for all men;
   this is his new commandment.

   Send forth your Spirit, O Lord.
   Send forth your Spirit on these your chosen ones.
   Send forth your Spirit of truth.

2. To know the will of the Father,
   to know the will of the Son,
   to know the Gospel of Jesus the Lord,
   to proclaim to everyone.

   Send forth your Spirit, O Lord.
   Send forth your Spirit on these your chosen ones.
   Send them to cast your fire on earth.

Verse 3   *Sung by Confirmation Candidates*

3. Come upon us, O Spirit of the living God!
   Come upon us, O Spirit of truth!
   Come upon us, O Spirit of love and life!
   Send us to cast your fire on earth!

   Send forth your Spirit, O Lord.
   Send forth your Spirit on these your chosen ones.
   Send them to cast your fire on earth.
   Send forth your Spirit, O Lord.
   Send forth your Spirit on these your chosen ones.
   Send forth your Spirit of love.

Words and music: Garfield Rochard
Harmony: for Celebration Hymnal
   by Eric Welch

©1981 Mayhew–McCrimmon Ltd

596

Refrain

Send forth your Spi-rit, O Lord, that the face of the earth be re-newed.

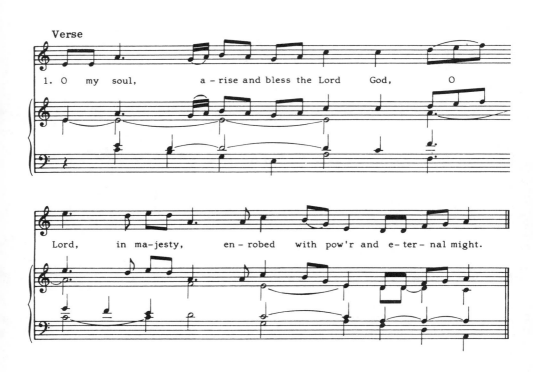

Verse

1. O my soul, a-rise and bless the Lord God, O

Lord, in ma-jesty, en-robed with pow'r and e-ter-nal might.

2. You are clothed with splendour and with beauty,
   O God, and heav'nly light
   is like a cloud that conceals your face.

3. You have built your palace on the waters;
   on wings of winds and fire
   you reign in heav'n, rule supreme on earth.

4. Like the winds your angels fly before you;
   as fire and flaming light,
   your ministers stand before your throne.

5. For the earth you fixed on its foundations;
   indeed, it shall stand firm,
   and not be moved for unending years.

6. On the earth the waters spread their mantle;
   and seas filled all the land;
   above the earth stood the rising flood.

7. When they heard on high your voice of thunder,
   in fear they took to flight;
   at your reproach, they dispersed and fled.

8. By your word, there sprang up hills and mountains;
   on earth the dry land rose,
   and in their place, rested glens and vales.

9. Your command sets bounds on all the waters,
   and they shall not return;
   they may not pass limits you have set.

10. Torrents fill the valleys at your order;
    while streams and rivers flow,
    refresh the beasts, slake the thirst of man.

11. From their nests, the birds give praise and glory
    to you, O Lord of hosts,
    from ev'ry branch, join in songs of praise.

12. In green fields you feed your sheep and cattle,
    and all your creatures, Lord;
    and yet to men, you have given more.

13. There is wine to cheer the heart of mankind;
    the wheat for man makes bread;
    and oil is used to anoint his head.

14. While I live, I sing the praise of Yahweh,
    O Lord, your glorious praise,
    my lips proclaim: Blessed be the Lord.

15. Praise to God, the author of these marvels,
    to God, the mighty One,
    who made the earth, glory to his name.

16. Praise to God, the Father, Son and Spirit,
    to God who gives us life,
    our thanks return, now and evermore.

Words: based on Psalm 103/4
by Lucien Deiss
Music: Lucien Deiss

597 NEUMARK (98 98 8 8)

Alternative tune: FRAGRANCE (545)

1. Shepherd of souls, in love come feed us.
   Life-giving bread for hungry hearts.
   To those refreshing waters lead us
   where dwells that grace your peace imparts.
   May we, the wayward in your fold,
   by your forgiveness rest consoled.

2. Life-giving vine, come, feed and nourish,
   strengthen each branch with life divine.
   Ever in you O may we flourish,
   fruitful the branches of the vine.
   Lord, may our souls be purified
   so that in Christ we may abide.

3. Sinful are we who stand before you
   worthy of you is Christ alone.
   So in Christ's name we do implore you;
   rich are the mercies you have shown.
   Say but the word, O Lord divine,
   then are our hearts made pure like thine.

4. Following you, O Lord, who led them,
   multitudes thronged the mountainside;
   filled with compassion, Lord, you fed them,
   fed them with loaves you multiplied.
   Come, feed us now, O Lord, we pray:
   lifegiving bread give us this day.

5. Help us, dear Lord, prepare a dwelling
   worthy of you who made us all;
   cleanse thou our hearts, our guilt dispelling,
   purify us who heed your call.
   'Take this and eat' were the words you said,
   so we have gathered for this bread.

Words: J.Clifford Evers
Music: George Neumark (1621-1681)
Harmony: J.S. Bach (1685-1759)

598

1. Show me your ways that I may fol- low you,

C   Am   Am   F6

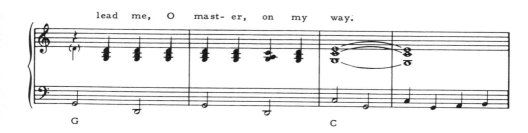

lead me, O mast- er, on my way.

G   C

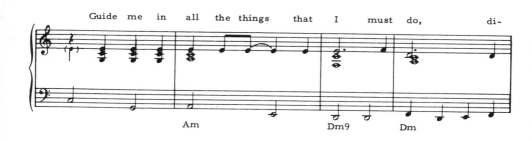

Guide me in all the things that I must do,   di-

Am   Dm9   Dm

rect my steps that I don't go a- stray.   Chorus
In

Fine

G   G7   C

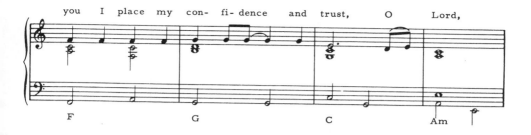

you   I place my con- fi- dence   and   trust,   O   Lord,

F   G   C   Am

have your way with me   for   I   am   yours.

F6   Dm   Dm7   G

D.C.

2. Guard me when temptation calls on me to sin.
   Protect me when the enemy is near.
   Strengthen me to turn to you that I may win,
   and bless me, Jesus, that I persevere.

Alternative Refrain:

   The spirit's willing but the flesh is weak, O Lord.
   But your support is all I'll ever need.

3. Show me your ways that I may follow you,
   lead me, O Master, on my way.
   Guide me in all the things that I must do,
   direct my steps that I don't go astray.

Words and Music: Sebastian Temple
Arrangement: Stephen Dean

599

1. Sing a simple song unto the Lord;
   sing a simple song unto the Lord,
   sing it with your heart, sing it with your soul,
   sing a simple song unto the Lord.

   Oh Lord, I love you;
   Oh Lord, I see;
   Oh Lord, I love you,
   I see that you love me.

2. Say a simple prayer ...

3. Give a simple gift ...

Words and Music: Carey Landry

600

1. Sing everyone a song to the Lord,
   a song to the Lord of all our hearts.
   He made us, we're the work of his hands,
   the work of his hands in all we are.
   Lord, we offer you
   everything we do,
   sing everyone a song to the Lord,
   a song to the Lord of all our hearts.

2. Come everyone who works for his life,
   who works for his life on this fair earth.
   He worked for us and left us himself,
   the gift of his life in bread and wine.
   Take our work and play,
   it's yours every day.
   Sing everyone a song to the Lord,
   a song to the Lord who makes us live.

3. Sing softly, for the Lord is around,
   he's there in the smallest summer breeze.
   Sing sweetly, for the Lord isn't harsh,
   he's gentle in voice, in giving, free.
   Lord, we love with you
   all those you give us now.
   Sing loudly, for the love of the Lord,
   the love of the Lord is all our joy.

Words and Music: Anne Conway

© Anne Conway

Harmony: for Celebration Hymnal
    by Eric Welch

© 1981 Mayhew-McCrimmon Ltd

601

Lively

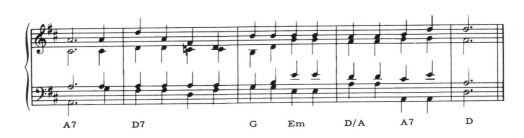

1. Sing praises to the Lord;
    sing praises to the Lord;
    sing praises to the Lord,
    alleluia, alleluia!

2. And holy be his Name;
    and holy be his Name;
    and holy be his Name,
    alleluia, alleluia!

3. For he is kind and good;
    for he is kind and good;
    for he is kind and good,
    alleluia, alleluia!

4. He died that we might live;
    he rose again to life;
    he lives no more to die,
    alleluia, alleluia!

Words and music: Derick Clouden
Harmony: for Celebration Hymnal
by Eric Welch

©1981 Mayhew—McCrimmon Ltd

602

Refrain

Sing to the Lord a song, sing to the Lord a psalm.

C   G7   C   Am   Dm   G7

Sing to the Lord, you na - tions! Praise his name!

Fine

C   G7   Am   Em   F   G7   C

Verse

He made hea-ven, he made the earth; the sea, the sky and

C   G7   C   E   Am   F   C/E

all there is. He made A-dam out of naught and

Dm7   G   C   G7   C   E   Am

told him these were his. *D.C.*

F   Dm   G7

2. Now, Adam was a lonely man,
   and God decided he would give
   a helping-mate to this new man:
   created the woman Eve.

3. Then God told Adam what to do:
   "Go forth, good man, into the world,
   multiply and fill the earth
   and bless my holy name".

Words and music: Helena Warner
Harmony: for Celebration Hymnal
          by Eric Welch

© 1981 Mayhew-McCrimmon Ltd

603

Bright and lively
Bright and lively
Response

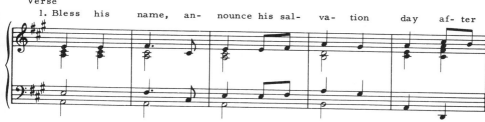

2. Give to him,
   you families of peoples
   glory and praise, alleluia.

3. Great is he,
   and worthy of praise
   day after day, alleluia.

4. He it is,
   who gave us the heavens,
   glory to God, alleluia.

5. Tell his glories,
   tell all the nations,
   day after day, alleluia.

6. Bring your gifts
   and enter his temple;
   worship the Lord, alleluia.

Words: based on Psalm 95, by John Foley, SJ
Music: John Foley, SJ, harmony by
Rosalind Pitcher

604

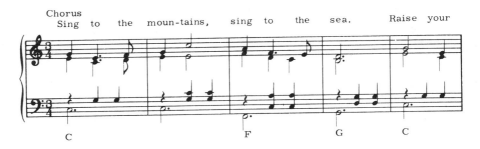

Chorus
Sing to the moun-tains, sing to the sea. Raise your

C   F   G   C

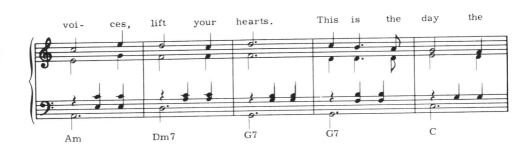

voi- ces, lift your hearts. This is the day the

Am   Dm7   G7   G7   C

Lord has made. Let all the earth re- joice.

fine

Em   A   D   G   C

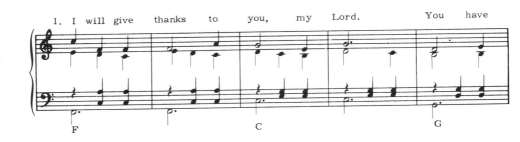

1. I will give thanks to you, my Lord. You have

F   C   G

an-swered my plea. You have saved my soul from

G7 C E E7 Am

death. You are my strength and my song.

D. C.

Am7 Dm G G7

2. Ho- ly, ho- ly, ho- ly Lord.

mp cresc.

Dm F C Dm C G

Hea- ven and earth are full of your glo- ry.

ff D. C.

E E7 Am Am7 Dm Dm7 G G7

Accompaniment as for Verse 1, followed by Chorus.

3. This is the day that the Lord has made.
   Let us be glad and rejoice.
   He has turned all death to life.
   Sing of the glory of God.

Words (based on Psalm 118) and Music: Bob Dufford, S.J.

605

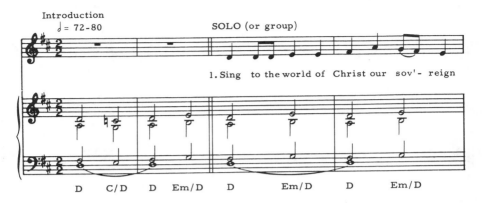

1. Sing to the world of Christ our sov'- reign

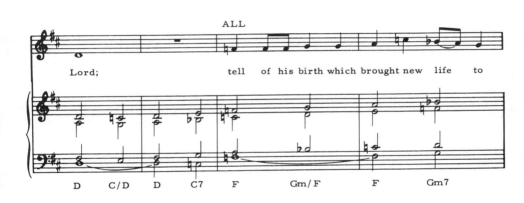

Lord; tell of his birth which brought new life to

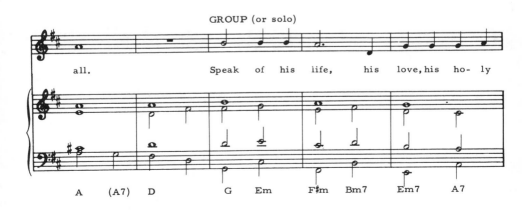

all. Speak of his life, his love, his ho- ly

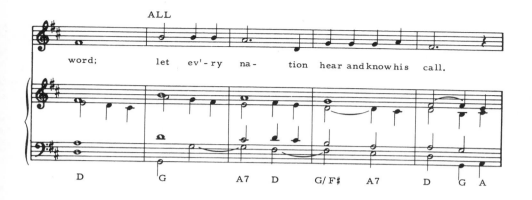

word;   let ev'- ry na-   tion hear and know his   call.

D   G   A7   D   G/F♯   A7   D   G   A

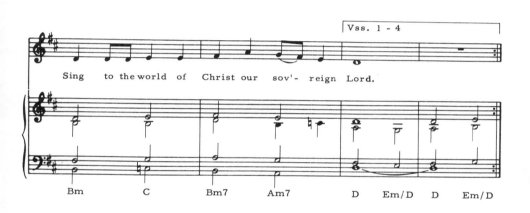

Vss. 1 - 4

Sing   to the world of   Christ our   sov'- reign Lord.

Bm   C   Bm7   Am7   D   Em/D   D   Em/D

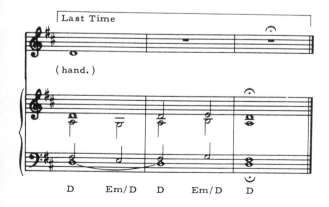

Last Time

(hand.)

D   Em/D   D   Em/D   D

2. Sing to the world of Christ the Prince of peace,
   showing to men the Father's loving care
   pleading that love should reign and wars might cease,
   teaching we need the love of God to share.
   Sing to the world of Christ the Prince of peace.

3. Sing to the world of Christ our steadfast friend,
   off'ring himself to live the constant sign;
   food for our souls until we meet life's end
   gives us his flesh for bread, his blood for wine.
   Sing to the world of Christ our steadfast friend.

4. Sing to the world of Christ our Saviour King,
   born that his death mankind's release should win;
   hung from a cross, forgiveness he could bring;
   buried, he rose to conquer death and sin.
   Sing to the world of Christ our Saviour King.

5. Sing to the world of Christ at God's right hand,
   praise to the Spirit both have sent to men,
   living in us till earth shall reach its span,
   time be no more, and Christ shall come again.
   Sing to the world of Christ at God's right hand.

Words: Patrick Lee
Music: Ernest Sands

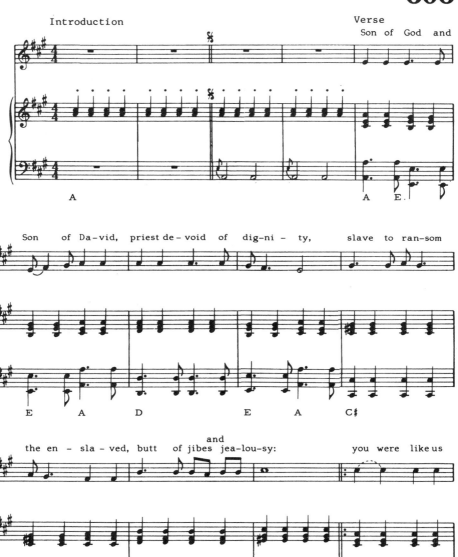

Introduction

Verse

Son of God and Son of Da-vid, priest de-void of dig-ni-ty, slave to ran-som the en-sla-ved, butt of jibes jea-lou-sy: and you were like us

and
strugg-ling try-ing   till your dy-ing   for our li-ber - ty.

Bm   E   A   E   D   E   A

- ty.   D.S.

2. Every creature should,
       with gladness,
   kneel before your majesty;
   every man, through joy
       and sadness,
   witness to your sanctity,
   bring you a rich credit balance
   from his talents
   and activity.

3. Jesus' name in condemnation
   nailed to that torturing tree,
   'King of Jews' that provocation
   you forgave in agony.
   Hear, Lord, this sinner's petition
   for remission
   life eternally.

Words: Ds Willem Barnard
       translated by Bonaventure Hinwood
Music: Ton Van Erp

D   A7   D

G   Em   A   D   A   Em   F♯m

Bm   A   D

Words: Fred Kaan
Music: Sri Lanka - popular melody

©1972 Fred Kaan

Harmony: for Celebration Hymnal
         by Frances M. & Robert B. Kelly

©1981 Mayhew-McCrimmon Ltd

1. Son of the Father, Jesus, Lord and slave,
   born among the cattle in the squalor of a cave,
   one with God, you made yourself one with man, shunning wealth;
   Lord, we worship you with heart and mind.

2. Son of the Father, Jesus, workers' friend,
   you whom Joseph taught the skills of working with your hands,
   man, at home in builder's yard, one with man, toiling hard;
   Lord, we worship you with hand and mind.

3. Son of the Father, author of our faith,
   choosing men to follow you from every walk of life,
   who with them, in boats, on shore, troubles shared, burdens bore;
   Lord, we worship you with hand and mind.

4. Seed of the Father, from life's furrow born,
   teaching men in parables from agriculture drawn,
   Jesus, lover of the soil, man of earth, son of toil;
   Lord, we worship you with hand and mind.

5. Father and Spirit, Jesus, Lord and Man,
   bless us in the work you have appointed to be done.
   Lift our spirits, guide our wills, steer our hands, use our skills;
   Lord, we worship you with hand and mind.

608

HEINLEIN 77. 77

1. Take my life and let it be con-se-cra-ted, Lord, to thee;

take my mo-ments and my days, let them flow in ceaseless praise.

2. Take my hands, and let them move
   at the impulse of thy love.
   Take my feet, and let them be
   swift and purposeful for thee.

3. Take my voice, and let me sing
   always, only for my King.
   Take my intellect, and use
   every power as thou shalt choose.

4. Take my will, and make it thine:
   it shall be no longer mine.
   Take my heart; it is thine own:
   it shall be thy royal throne.

5. Take my love; my Lord, I pour
   at thy feet its treasure-store.
   Take myself, and I will be
   ever, only, all for thee.

Words: Frances R. Havergal (1836-1879)
Music: Probably by Martin Herbst (1654-1681),
       harmony by A. Gregory Murray

Music © Burns and Oates Ltd

609

1. Tell out, my soul, the great-ness of the Lord! Un-
num- bered bless-ings, give my spi- rit voice; ten- der to
me the prom-ise of his word; in God my
Sa- viour shall my heart re- joice.

2. Tell out, my soul, the greatness of his name!
   Make known his might, the deeds his arm has done;
   his mercy sure, from age to age the same;
   his holy name - the Lord, the Mighty One.

3. Tell out, my soul, the greatness of his might!
   Powers and dominions lay their glory by.
   Proud hearts and stubborn wills are put to flight,
   the hungry fed, the humble lifted high.

4. Tell out, my soul, the glories of his word!
   Firm is his promise, and his mercy sure.
   Tell out, my soul, the greatness of the Lord
   to children's children and for evermore!

Words: Timothy Dudley-Smith,
based on Luke 1:46-55
Music: Walter Greatorex 1877-1949

610

our Re - deem-er King, he is the Lord of Lords: .

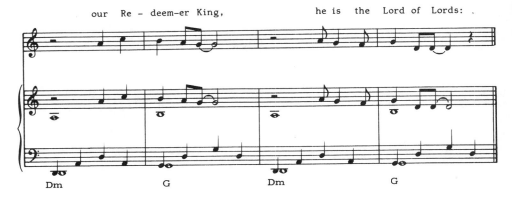

Dm G Dm G

3. He is the bread of life;
    wonder-counsellor;
    he is Prince of peace.

Words: based on 1 John 1:1
       by Carey Landry
Music: Carey Landry

611

1. The angel Gabriel from heaven came,
   his wings as drifted snow, his eyes as flame;
   'All hail,' said he, 'thou lowly maiden Mary,
   most highly favoured lady,
   Gloria!

2. 'For known a blessed Mother thou shalt be,
   all generations laud and honour thee,
   thy Son shall be Emmanuel, by seers foretold;
   most highly favoured lady.'
   Gloria!

3. Then gentle Mary meekly bowed her head,
   'To me be as it pleaseth God,' she said,
   'my soul shall laud and magnify his holy name':
   most highly favoured lady,
   Gloria!

4. Of her, Emmanuel, the Christ was born
   in Bethlehem, all on a Christmas morn,
   and christian folk throughout the world will ever say
   'most highly favoured lady'.
   Gloria!

Basque Carol paraphrased by Sabine Baring-Gould 1834-1924

Music © EMI Music Publishing Ltd,
138-140 Charing Cross Rd, London WC2H OLD

612

1. The Church is wherever God's people are easing
   burdens of others in love and good will.
   The Church is wherever the cross of the Saviour
   is borne by believers who follow him still.

2. The Church is wherever God's people are trusting;
   facing hard trials with hope, not despair.
   The Church is wherever a miracle follows
   beyond human power, in answer to prayer.

3. The Church is wherever his own come to Jesus,
   stirred by a longing and need to be whole.
   The Church is wherever God's people adore him
   in worship that rises from heart, mind and soul.

4. The Church is wherever disciples of Jesus
   turn to their Master each step of the way.
   The Church is wherever the love of the Saviour
   is seen in his followers' lives day by day.

Words: Pat Regehr
Music: A. Gregory Murray

CONSOLATION (86.86)

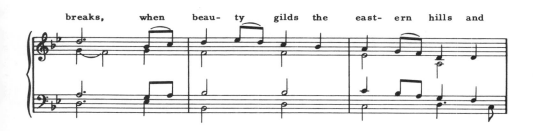

2. Not as of old a little child,
   to bear and fight and die,
   but crowned with glory like the sun
   that lights the morning sky.

3. O brighter than the rising morn
   when he, victorious, rose,
   and left the lonesome place of death,
   despite the rage of foes.

4. O brighter than that glorious morn
   shall this fair morning be,
   when Christ our King in beauty comes,
   and we his face shall see!

5. The King shall come when morning dawns
   and light and beauty brings;
   'Hail, Christ the Lord!' your people pray,
   'Come quickly, King of kings!'

Words: John Brownlie 1859-1925
Music: Kentucky Harmony 1816

614

The light of Christ has come in- to the world, the

The light of Christ has come in to the world,

C   F   Dm   G

Fine

light of Christ has come in- to the world.

the light of Christ has come.

C   F   G   C

Fine

**The light of Christ has come into the world,
the light of Christ has come into the world.**

1. All men must be born again to see the kingdom of God:
   the water and the Spirit bring new life in God's love.

2. God gave up his only Son out of love for the world
   so that ev'ryone who believes in him will live for ever.

3. The Light of God has come to us so that we might have salvation,
   from the darkness of our sins we walk into glory with Christ Jesus.

Words and Music: Donald Fisher

1. The Lord is my shepherd.
   He provides all I need
   in the rich grassland,
   where he lets me feed.
   He brings me to water
   my life to renew.
   He guides me on true paths
   because he is true.

2. I walk through the darkness,
   with nothing to fear;
   his right hand protects me
   when danger is near.
   He lays me a table
   in spite of my foes.
   He fills me with gladness,
   my cup overflows.

3. Each day he is goodness,
   each day he's my song.
   I live in his household
   the whole of life long.
   The Lord is my shepherd.
   He provides all I need
   in the rich grassland,
   where he lets me feed.

Words: based on Psalm 22/3
by Hubert Richards
Music: Hubert Richards

© 1970 Mayhew McCrimmon Ltd

616

The seed is Christ's, the har-vest his: may we be stored wi-

thin God's barn. The sea is Christ's, the fish are his: may we be caught wi-

thin God's net. From birth to age, from age to death, en-

fold us, Christ, wi- thin your arms. Un- til the end, the

great re- birth, Christ be our joy in Pa- ra-dise.

Words: translated from the Gaelic and
adapted by James Quinn SJ

© Geoffrey Chapman

Music © Sean O'Riada

617

The Spi-rit is mo-ving all o - ver, all o - ver this land.

Verse

The style of this hymn is very free; the cantor adopts the
rhythm for the words of the verses that suit him best.
The accompanist must make the necessary allowances.

**The Spirit is moving all over,
all over this land.**

1. People are gathering, the Church is born;
   the Spirit is blowing on a world reborn.

2. Doors are opening as the Spirit comes;
   his fire is burning in his people now.

3. Filled with his Spirit we are sent to serve;
   we are called out as brothers, we are called to work.

4. The world, born once, is born again;
   we recreate it in love and joy.

5. Old men are dreaming dreams;
   and young men see the light.

6. Old walls are falling down;
   and people are speaking with each other.

7. The Spirit fills us with his power
   to be his witnesses to all we meet.

8. The Spirit urges us to travel light
   to be people of courage who spread his fire.

9. God has poured out his Spirit
   on all; on all creation.

Words and Music: Carey Landry

618

1. The Spi- rit lives to set us free, walk, walk in the light. He binds us all in u- ni- ty, walk, walk in the light.

Chorus
Walk in the light, walk in the light, walk in the light, walk in the light of the Lord.

2. Jesus promised life to all,
walk, walk in the light.
The dead were wakened by his call,
walk, walk in the light.

3. He died in pain on Calvary,
walk, walk in the light,
to save the lost like you and me,
walk, walk in the light.

4. We know his death was not the end,
walk, walk in the light.
He gave his Spirit to be our friend,
walk, walk in the light.

5. By Jesus' love our wounds are healed,
walk, walk in the light.
The Father's kindness is revealed,
walk, walk in the light.

6. The Spirit lives in you and me,
walk, walk in the light.
His light will shine for all to see,
walk, walk in the light.

Words: Damian Lundy
Music: Unknown, arranged by Michael Irwin

619

The Spi-rit of God rests up-on me, the Spi-rit of God consecrates

Gm   Dm Eb   Bb Gm   Dm Gm   Cm

me the Spi-rit of God bids me go forth to pro-claim his peace, his joy.   Verse
1. The

Dm Gm Eb Bb   Gm   Eb Bb Cm   G

Spirit of God sends me forth, called to   witness the kingdom of Christ among all the

Gm   Dm   Eb   Bb   F Cm Eb7   Bb Gm F

na-tions; called to pro-claim the good news of Christ to the poor.   My

Cm Gm Dm   F   Cm   Gm Bb

2. The Spirit of God sends me forth,
   called to witness the kingdom of Christ
   among all the nations;
   called to console
   the hearts overcome with great sorrow.
   My spirit rejoices in God, my Saviour.

3. The Spirit of God sends me forth,
   called to witness the kingdom of Christ
   among all the nations;
   called to comfort
   the poor who mourn and who weep.
   My spirit rejoices in God, my Saviour.

4. The Spirit of God sends me forth,
   called to witness the kingdom of Christ
   among all the nations;
   called to announce
   the grace of salvation to men.
   My spirit rejoices in God, my Saviour.

5. The Spirit of God sends me forth,
   called to witness the kingdom of Christ
   among all the nations;
   called to reveal
   his glory among all the people.
   My spirit rejoices in God, my Saviour.

Words: based on Isaiah 61: 1-2 & Luke 4: 18-19,
        by Lucien Deiss
Music: Lucien Deiss

620

There is a ri-ver that flows from God a-bove,

G · C · G · C · E7

there is a fountain that's filled with his great love.

Am · D7 · G · D7

Chorus

Come to the wa-ters, there is a great sup-ply,

G · C · G · C · E7

there is a ri-ver that ne-ver shall run dry.

Am · D7 · Am · D7 · G

2. Wash me with water, and then I shall be clean;
   white as the new snow, if you remove my sin. (Psalm 50)

3. Plunged in the water, the tomb of our rebirth,
   so may we rise up to share in Christ's new life.

4. All who are thirsty, now hear God as he calls;
   come to the Lord's side, his life pours out for all. (Jn.19:33-35)

5. Safe in the new Ark, the Church of Christ our Lord,
   praise God for water, his sign to save the world.

Words: Verse 1 traditional
       Verses 2-5 Robert B.Kelly

© 1980 Mayhew-McCrimmon Ltd

Harmony: Stephen Dean

© Mayhew-McCrimmon Ltd

Refrain (voice parts)

1. Verse

2.

3.

There is one Lord,
there is one faith,
there is one baptism,
one God, who is Father.

1.   We were called to be one
     in the Spirit of God,
in the bond of peace,
     we sing and proclaim.

2.   We were called to form one body
     in one spirit,
we sing and proclaim.

3.   We were called in the same hope
     in Christ the Lord,
we sing and proclaim.

Words: based on Ephesians 4
     by Lucien Deiss
Music: Lucien Deiss

622

1. Thine be the glo- ry, ris- en conquering Son,

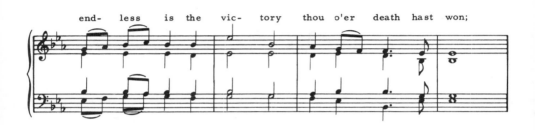

end- less is the vic- tory thou o'er death hast won;

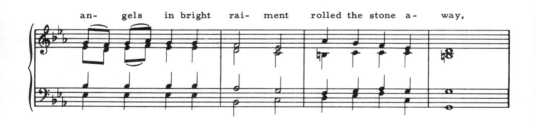

an- gels in bright rai- ment rolled the stone a- way,

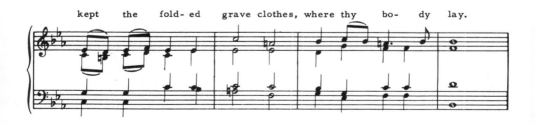

kept the fold- ed grave clothes, where thy bo- dy lay.

Refrain

Refrain
Thine be the glo- ry, ris- en, conquering Son,

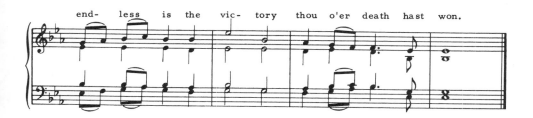

end- less is the vic- tory thou o'er death hast won.

2. Lo, Jesus meets us, risen from the tomb;
   lovingly he greets us, scatters fear and gloom;
   let the church with gladness, hymns of triumph sing,
   for her Lord is living, death has lost its sting.

Refrain

3. No more we doubt thee, glorious Prince of life;
   life is nought without thee: aid us in our strife;
   make us more than conquerors, through thy deathless love:
   bring us safe through Jordan to thy home above.

Refrain

Words: Edmund Louis Budry 1854-1932, translated by
        Richard Birch Hoyle 1875-1939
Music: Adapted from George Frederick Handel 1685-1759

623

1. This is my bo-dy, bro-ken for you,

Capo 1 Dmaj7 G   Dmaj7 G   Dmaj7   G   Dmaj7   G

bring-ing you wholeness, ma-king you free. Take it and eat it,

Dmaj7   G   Em   A7   Em   A7

and when you do,   do it in love for   me.

F#m   Bm   G   Em A7 Dmaj7 G

2. This is my blood poured out for you,
   bringing forgiveness, making you free.
   Take it and drink it, and when you do,
   do it in love for me.

3. Back to my Father soon I shall go.
   Do not forget me; then you will see
   I am still with you, and you will know
   you're very close to me.

4. Filled with my Spirit, how you will grow!
   You are my branches; I am the tree.
   If you are faithful, others will know
   you are alive in me.

5. Love one another - I have loved you,
   and I have shown you how to be free;
   serve one another, and when you do,
   do it in love for me.

Words: Verses 1 and 2 Jimmy Owens,
verses 3—5 Damian Lundy
Music: Jimmy Owens

This is the day
that the Lord has made,
let us rejoice and shout
"Alleluia!"

1. We were asleep,
   it seemed like death
   but now the morning's broken.

2. The winter's past,
   the grass is green
   and Spring is life in our land.

3. The Lord of life
   has passed through death
   and still he lives among us.

Words: based on Psalm 117/8
by Anne Conway
Music: Anne Conway

© 1977 Anne Conway

Harmony: for Celebration Hymnal
by Frances M. & Robert B. Kelly

625

1. This is the day; **this is the day;**
   that the Lord has made; **that the Lord has made.**
   We will rejoice; **we will rejoice;**
   and be glad in it; **and be glad in it.**
   This is the day that the Lord has made;
   we will rejoice and be glad in it.
   This is the day, this is the day
   that the Lord has made.

2. This is the day
   when he rose again ...

3. This is the day
   when the Spirit came ...

Author unknown

Verse

This is the feast of vict'ry for our God
for the Lamb who was slain
    has begun his reign
has begun his reign, alleluia!
This is the feast of vict'ry for our God
for the Lamb who was slain
has begun his reign, alleluia!

1. Worthy is Christ, the Lamb who was slain,
   whose blood set us free to be People of God.
   Power, riches, wisdom and strength
   and honour, blessing and glory are his.

2. Sing with all the People of God
   and join in the hymn of all creation:
   Blessing, honour, glory and might
   be to God and the Lamb for ever.
       Amen.

Words: based on Revelation 4:9-14
       by John Ylvisaker
Music: John Ylvisaker

Harmony: for Celebration Hymnal
       by Frances M. & Robert B. Kelly

♩ = 64

mf

1. This is the night   when God de — li — vered our fore-
2. This is the night   the pillar of fire be-comes a

G

fa - thers from their chains,   led them dry - shod through the sea,
bea - con of be — lief   to lead the peo - ple on,   when

C   G   C   G

out of sla - ver - y.   Free your peo - ple once a - gain.
hope is near - ly gone,   un - wav'r - ing joy con-sum-ing grief.

Em   D7   G   C   Bm   Am   D7   G

This is the night (This is the night) when Christ has ran-somed us and
this is the night of nights a-

D

paid the price of sin. The Pas-chal Lamb was slain, bring-ing peace through
wait-ed since the Fall, when death is our re-birth, with heav-en wed to

C   G   C   G   Am   D7

pain. We will fol-low where he's been. This is the
earth, re — con — cil-ling one and all.

Em   C   D   C D7 C .D7 G

night (This is the night) this is the night he rose tri - um - phant from the
this is the night of joy, of sol - emn songs of

D G   D7   G   Bm7   C   D7

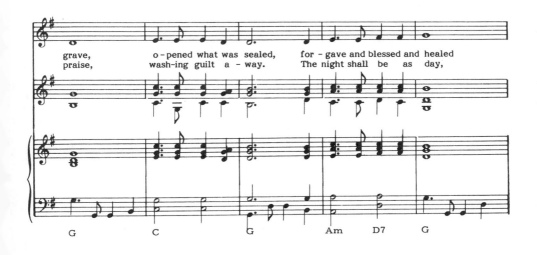

grave,   o - pened what was sealed,   for - gave and blessed and healed
praise,   wash-ing guilt a - way.   The night shall be   as   day,

G   C   G   Am   D7   G

those he suf-fered death to save. O hap-py fault!

mourning turned to danc-ing all our days. O hap-py

O hap-py fault.

Bm   Am   D7   G

O nec-es-sa-ry sin! A new day rush — es in!

fault! Nec-es-sa-ry sin! A new day rush — es in!

G   C   G   C   D7   G

new day rush —— es

new day rush —— es

C   D7

in!

in!

G

Words: based on the Easter Preconium
       by Miriam Therese Winter
Music: Miriam Therese Winter

628

Refrain

This is what Yah – weh asks of you, on – ly

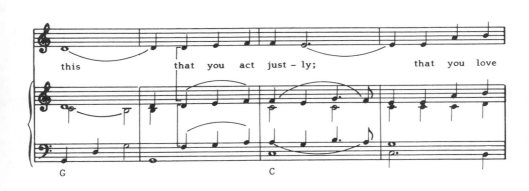

this that you act just – ly; that you love

ten – der – ly, that you walk hum – bly

with your God.

G

C

Am

FINE

1. "My

Dm

G

Verses

(V3 ♩. ♪♩)

1. chil - dren I am with you such a lit-tle while,
2. "Do not let your hearts be trou - bled:
3. "Peace is the gift I leave with you,

G

F

C

and where I go now, you can - not
trust in God now, and trust in
a peace the world can ne - ver

Dm   G

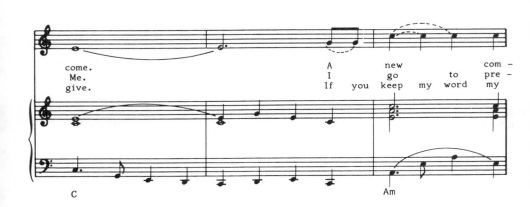

come. A new com -
Me. I go to pre -
give. If you keep my word my

C   Am

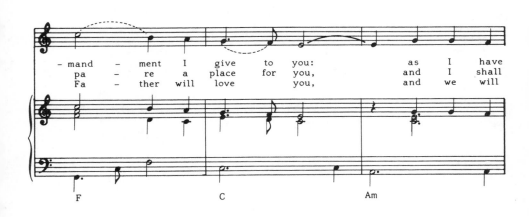

- mand - ment I give to you: as I have
pa - re a place for you, and I have
Fa - ther will love you, and we shall

F   C   Am

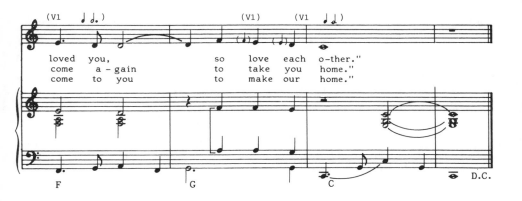

loved you, so love each o-ther."
come a – gain to take you home."
come to you to make our home."

F   G   C   D.C.

Words and Music: Mary McGann RSCJ

© 1974 Ephpheta House, 3330 Adams Road,
Auburn Heights, Michigan 48057, USA.

Arranged by Rosalind Pitcher

© 1984 Mayhew-McCrimmon Ltd

629

MOSCOW 664. 6664

2. Thou who didst come to bring
on thy redeeming wing
healing and sight,
health to the sick in mind,
sight to the inly blind,
ah! now to all mankind
let there be light!

3. Spirit of truth and love,
life-giving, holy dove,
speed forth thy flight!
Move on the waters' face,
bearing the lamp of grace,
and in earth's darkest place
let there be light!

4. Blessed and holy Three,
glorious Trinity,
wisdom, love, might;
boundless as ocean tide
rolling in fullest pride,
through the world far and wide
let there be light!

Words: J. Marriott (1780-1825)
Music: Adapted from F. de Giardini (1716-96)

Chorus

Though the moun- tains may fall and the hills turn to dust,

Capo 3 (D)   G   D   C

yet the love of the Lord will stand

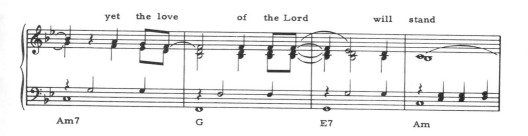

Am7   G   E7   Am

as a shel- ter for all who will call on his name.

D   G   D   C

Sing the praise and the glo- ry of God.

fine

Am7   G   D   C   G

Verses
More gently
1. Could the Lord ever leave you? Could the Lord forget his love? Though the mother forsake her child, he will not abandon you.

D.C.

2. Should you turn and forsake him,
   he will gently call your name.
   Should you wander away from him,
   he will always take you back.

3. Go to him when you're weary;
   he will give you eagle's wings.
   You will run, never tire,
   for your God will be your strength.

4. As he swore to your Fathers,
   when the flood destroyed the land.
   He will never forsake you;
   he will swear to you again.

Words (based on Isaiah) and Music: Dan Schutte, S.J.

WILTSHIRE (86.86)

1. Through all the changing scenes of life,
   in trouble and in joy,
   the praises of my God shall still
   my heart and tongue employ.

2. Of his deliverance I will boast,
   till all that are distressed,
   when learning this, will comfort take
   and calm their griefs to rest.

3. O magnify the Lord with me,
   with me exalt his name;
   when in distress to him I called
   he to my rescue came.

4. The hosts of God encamp around
   the dwellings of the just;
   deliverance he affords to all
   who on his succour trust.

5. O make but trial of his love;
   experience will decide
   how blest are they, and only they,
   who in his truth confide.

6. Fear him, ye saints, and you will then
   have nothing else to fear;
   make you his service your delight,
   your wants shall be his care.

Words: Psalm 34
        paraphrased by Natum Tate (1652–1715)
        adapted by Anthony G. Petti
Music: George T. Smart (1776–1867)

632

To be the body of the Lord in this world,
to have his Spirit coursing through my soul,
to know the passion of my Jesus
in his love for every man,
to show his mercy in the shadows of this land.

Verse

1. Come, walk with me; come, share my life,
   you must know the shadows
   if you would know the light.

2. No eyes have I, no ears to hear,
   you must be my Body and show
   my Father's care.

3. Open your eyes, see what I see.
   For this world how I suffer.
   Share my destiny.

4. I am the vine, branches are you.
   Life from me eternal to make
   your world anew.

5. One bread, one cup; one heart and mind.
   One great human people
   in fellowship divine.

Words and music: Clyde Harvey
Harmony: for Celebration Hymnal
by Eric Welch

rit.................

1. To God our Father be the praise,
   be glory ever given,
   for to this world he sent his Son
   that we might be forgiven.

2. The world in sin and darkness lay;
   goodness was put to flight;
   and in the fulness of his time
   God sent his Son, the Light.

3. "In him was life" the Gospel says,
   "this life was light of men."
   The darkness has been overcome,
   the Light of God shines on.

4. The Light of God is in the world,
   but shines not everywhere;
   he shines alone in human lives
   when he's invited there.

5. "Behold at the door of your life I stand
   the Light, the Life, the Love;
   I will come in," he says, "and will
   illuminate your soul."

6. Rejoice then, you who sing this hymn;
   real life, real joy and light
   shall be for you eternally,
   if you will welcome him.

Words: William Armitage
Music: Bill Tamblyn

Words   © 1977 William Armitage
Music   © 1980 Bill Tamblyn

634

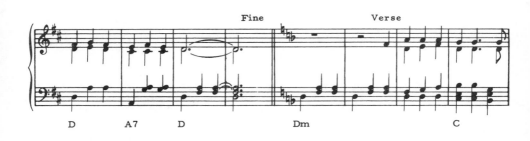

G   D   A   D   A7   D

Together we journey on the highway of God,
to the mountain of glory and grace;
and together we'll seek for the pearl of great price
till we meet with the Lord face to face.

1. There's one on that journey who's burdened with sorrow,
   bitterness hidden by grief:
   yet we shall bear it, together we'll share it,
   united in heart and in mind.

2. Another who travels is joyful and trusting,
   clothed with the garment of peace:
   so we shall wear it, together we'll share it,
   united in heart and in mind.

3. And all we who journey have gladness and sorrow
   somewhere on God's holy way:
   so we shall bear them, together we'll share them,
   united in heart and in mind.

Words and music: John Glynn

©1978 John Glynn

Harmony: for Celebration Hymnal
         by John Rombaut

©1981 Mayhew—McCrimmon Ltd

635

Introduction ♩ = 105　　　　　Antiphon

Trust in the Lord; you shall not tire. Serve you the Lord; you shall not weak-en. For the Lord's own strength will up-hold you. You shall re-new your life and live. (Verse 1)

Verse 2

2. Young hearts may grow faint and weak. Youths may col- lapse, stum-ble and fall. They that hope in the Lord will re-

new their cour-age. They'll soar with ea- gle's might. (Antiphon)

3. Old men shall dream new dreams;
   young men will find wisdom in visions.
   The Lord will speak in our lifetime,
   show his face to those who wait.

Words and Music: Robert F. O'Connor, S.J.

636

Refrain (Harmony)
Fine

U – nite us Lord, in peace and up – hold us with your love.

Gm   Cm   F   Gm   Cm   F   Gm

Verse (Unison)
can
1. Our faults di-vide and hin-der; your grace make us one; we won-der at your

Gm   F   Dm   Cm

is
ri-sing, your light like the sun.

Gm   F   Eb6   D

2. You are our expectation in loneliness and pain;
   your healing and your pardon are greater than our sin.

3. Lord, look upon the starving and set the captive free.
   Share out among our brothers the bread of unity.

4. How happy are the people who strive to be at one,
   who learn to live as brothers, who lay their hatred down.

5. O Lord, whose silent spirit enlightens and endows,
   make us in faith receptive and help us love your house.

6. Your cross will draw together the circle of mankind;
   in you shall all the people their true communion find.

7. Death can no longer hurt us, triumphant is your word.
   Let life now grow and blossom, O Jesus, risen Lord!

Words: Dominique Ombrie
       translated by Fred Kaan
Music: Dominique Ombrie

Words © 1972 Fred Kaan
Music © SEFIM (D87)

DANBY (88.88)

1. Up- on thy ta- ble, Lord, we place these sym-bols

Unison

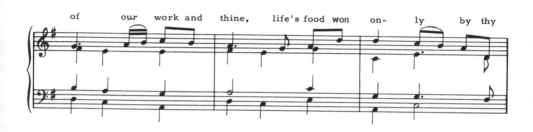

of our work and thine, life's food won on- ly by thy

grace, who giv'st to all the bread and wine.

2. Within these simple things there lie
the height and depth of human life,
the thought of man, his tears and toil,
his hope and fears, his joy and strife.

3. Accept them, Lord; from thee they come:
we take them humbly at thy hand.
These gifts of thine for higher use
we offer, as thou dost command.

Words: M.F.C. Willson 1884–1944
Music: Traditional English melody,
harmony © Stephen Dean

638

This was sung as the Entrance and Confirmation chants for the Papal Mass at Coventry Airport on Pentecost Sunday, May 30th 1982.

Establish the congregational refrain firmly before adding the solo part.* The refrain continues under each of the five verses and may be repeated at the end softly.
The congregation should sing quietly and prayerfully while the soloist sings according to the natural stresses of the words in the verses.
If desired a pleasing variation is to perform it with guitar accompaniment with the solo part taken by a flute. If desired the whole could be transposed into D with no capo.

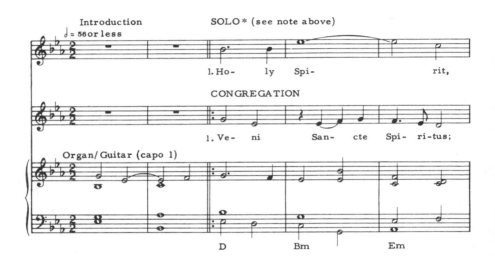

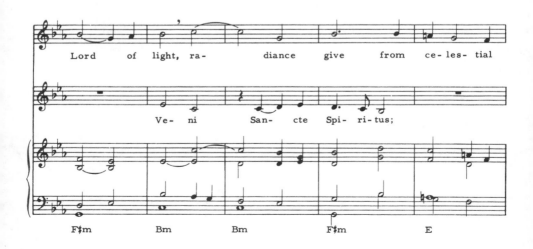

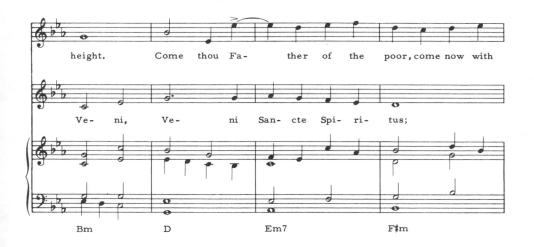

height. Come thou Fa- ther of the poor, come now with

Ve- ni, Ve- ni San- cte Spi- ri- tus;

Bm   D   Em7   F♯m

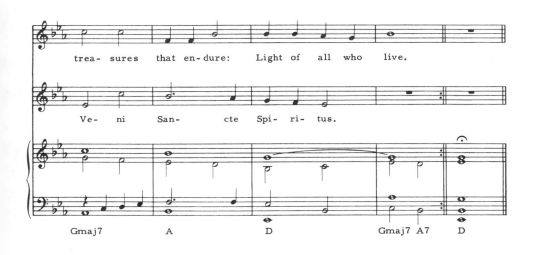

trea- sures that en- dure: Light of all who live.

Ve- ni San- cte Spi- ri- tus.

Gmaj7   A   D   Gmaj7 A7   D

Verses 2 - 5 over

4. Heal our wounds our strength re- new, on our dry- ness pour thy dew; wash guilt a- way, bend the stub- born heart, melt the fro- zen, warm the chill and guide the steps that go a- stray.

5. Seven- fold gifts on us be pleased to pour, who thee con- fess and thee a- dore; bring us thy com- fort when we die; give us life with thee on high; give us joys, give us joys that ne- ver end.

Words altered by Christopher Walker
from the version by Edward Caswall (1814-78).
Music by Christopher Walker

639

WACHET AUF (898.D.664.88)

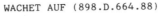

1st time | 2nd time

1. 'Wake, awake! For night is dying,'
   the watchmen on the heights are crying,
   'Awake, Jerusalem, at last!'
   Midnight hears the welcome voices,
   and at the thrilling cry rejoices:
   'Come forth, you virgins, night is past;
   the bridegroom comes; awake,
   your lamps with gladness take,
   hallelujah!
   and for his marriage feast prepare,
   for you must go to meet him there.'

2. Sion hears the watchmen singing,
   and all her heart with joy is springing;
   she wakes, she rises from her gloom:
   for her Lord comes down all-glorious,
   the strong in grace, in truth victorious;
   her star is risen, her light is come.
   Now come, O blessed one,
   God's own beloved Son;
   hallelujah!
   we follow to the festal hall
   to sup with you, the Lord of all.

3. Now let earth and heavens adore you,
   as men and angels sing before you
   with harp and cymbal's joyful tone;
   of one pearl each shining portal,
   where we join with choirs immortal
   of angels round your dazzling throne.
   No eye has seen, nor ear
   is yet attuned to hear,
   such great glory;
   hallelujah, as here we sing
   our praise to you, eternal King!

Words: Philip Nicolai (1556-1608)
       cento translation by Anthony G. Petti
       based on Catherine Winkworth (1827-78)
Music: Melody by Philip Nicolai,
       adapted and harmonised by J.S. Bach (1685-1750)

640

Wake up! the dawn is near;
no time for sleeping, this:
our God is sending us his gift,
his Son, the Lord of bliss.

1. Come, Lord of all the world,
   creation's source and sum;
   break through these barren, wintry skies
   and show your mercy – come!

2. Our sins are multiplied,
   yet yours alone we stand –
   you shaped us as the clay is shaped
   beneath the potter's hand.

3. See how we stray from you,
   so deeply have we sinned,
   swept on by wickedness, like leaves
   before the autumn wind.

4. Yet still we trust your word,
   your pardon precious-priced,
   your wisdom sweetly ruling all,
   the chosen one, your Christ.

Words: Luke Connaughton
Music: Eric Welch

641

Verse

Em   Am   Em   **Start here**   B7

Refrain

Em   B7   Em

D   Em   B7   Em

B7   Em

Words: Psalm 105
    paraphrased by John C. Ylvisaker
Music: Traditional American
    arranged by John C. Ylvisaker

©1979 John C. Ylvisaker

Harmony: for Celebration Hymnal
    by John Rombaut

©1981 Mayhew-McCrimmon Ltd

We are bound for the promised land, we're bound for the promised land;
Oh, who will come and go with us? We are bound for the promised land.

1. We seek you, Lord, and all your strength
    your presence constantly,
    rememb'ring all your marv'lous works,
    and all that you can be.

2. You are the Lord, you are the God
    whose judgements fill this earth;
    you're mindful of your covenant;
    we can trust you at your Word.

3. To Abraham you made a vow,
    a promise to his son:
    "I'll give to you the promised land!
    Your inheritance is won."

4. Give glory to the Father, Son,
    and Spirit, One in Three;
    as it was in the beginning,
    it shall forever be.

642

Refrain

A   F#m   Dmaj7   E

| Where verse follows | Last time |

A   F#m   D   E   A

1. Be-hold our Sa-viour comes. Be-hold the Son of our God. He

A   D   A   D   E

off-ers him-self and he comes a-mong us, a low-ly ser-vant to men.

Bm   E   A   F#m   D   E

We cry, "Hosanna, Lord," yes, "Hosanna, Lord,"
yes, "Hosanna, Lord" to you.
We cry, "Hosanna, Lord," yes, "Hosanna, Lord,"
yes, "Hosanna, Lord," to you.

2.   Children wave their palms
as the King of all kings rides by.
Should we forget to praise our God,
the very stones would sing.

3.   He comes to set us free.
He gives us liberty.
His vict'ry over death is
th'eternal sign of God's love for us.

Words and music: Mimi Farra

643

Words: Willard F. Jabusch
Music: American traditional

©1976 Willard F. Jabusch

Harmony: for Celebration Hymnal
by John Rombaut

© 1981 Mayhew-McCrimmon Ltd

1. We form one Church, one Christian folk, redeemed by God's own Son;
   refreshed by clear and saving streams, we share in graces won.
   We break the Bread of heaven to feed us on our way,
   we take the cup that holds his blood to celebrate his day.

2. We know the kindness of his love; we know his will to save;
   we know he's won the victory o'er sin and o'er the grave.
   To each of us is given the fullness of his grace,
   to live in joy a life of love until we see his face.

3. Our hope is based on Jesus Christ, our faith is in his name;
   we know he seeks the sinful one, for that is why he came;
   he cares for those who suffer, he loves both young and old,
   a man of sorrows, risen now, as he himself foretold!

644

KREMSER (12.11.12.12)

1. We gather together to ask the Lord's blessing, he
chastens and hastens his will to make known; the
wicked oppressing now cease from distressing, sing
praises to his Name; he forgets not his own.

* these notes are tied in vv 2-3, in v 2 on 'all', in v 3 on 'O'.

2. Beside us to guide us, our God with us joining,
   ordaining, maintaining his kingdom divine;
   so from the beginning the fight we were winning:
   Thou, Lord, wast at our side: all glory be thine!

3. We all do extol thee, thou leader triumphant,
   and pray that thou still our defender wilt be.
   Let thy congregation escape tribulation:
   Thy Name ever praised! O Lord, make us free!

Words: Theodore Baker (1851–1934)
Words permission of G.Schirmer, Inc.

645

1. We praise you and thank you our Father above,
   who offer us peace in your kingdom of love.
   Your people are saved by the death of your Son
   who leads us to glory where all will be one.
   Accepting this Gospel we honour Saint Patrick,
   who taught in our land what your kindness has done.

2. Your Word has revealed what our future will be
   'Raised up from the earth I draw all men to me.
   May we, like Saint Patrick, bear witness to you,
   reflecting your love in whatever we do.
   He came to our country which once had enslaved him,
   to preach the good news that God makes all things new.

Words: Donal Murray
Music: Traditional

©Donal Murray

646

SONG 1 (10.10.10.10.10.10)

TE DEUM LAUDAMUS

1. We praise you, God, confessing you as Lord!
   Eternal Father, all earth worships you!
   Angelic choirs, high heavens, celestial powers,
   cherubs and seraphs praise you ceaselessly:
   "All-holy Lord, O God of heavenly hosts,
   your glorious majesty fills heaven and earth."

2. Blessed apostles join in praise of you
   with prophets famed and martyrs clothed in white,
   singing with holy Church throughout the earth:
   "Father, we praise your boundless majesty!
   We praise your glorious, true and only Son!
   We praise you, Holy Spirit, Paraclete!"

3. You are the King of glory, Jesus Christ!
   You are the Father's everlasting Son!
   Born for mankind from lowly Virgin's womb,
   death you have conquered, opening heaven to faith;
   throned now in glory at the Father's side
   you shall return in glory as our judge.

4. We pray you, therefore, give your servants aid,
   whom you have ransomed with your precious blood,
   let them be ranked in glory with your saints;
   save, Lord, the people who are wholly yours,
   bless them, for they are your inheritance,
   and, as their ruler, ever raise them up.

5. Throughout each single day, we bless you Lord,
   for all eternity we praise your name.
   Keep us this day, Lord, free from every sin;
   have mercy on us, Lord; have mercy, Lord;
   show us your love, as we have hoped in you!
   You are my hope, Lord; you shall fail me not!

Words © 1969 James Quinn SJ
printed by permission of Geoffrey Chapman,
a division of Cassell Ltd
Music: Orlando Gibbons (1583-1625)

647

and   joy,   for   all of us   who share in

G7   Am   C

* *Last time to Coda*

1.   **Verse**

your won-der-ful   love each day.   harmony To live in the

mel.

Spi-rit is to grow in lib-er-   ty.   With-out love our free-dom

Em   F   G7   C   Em

*Final Ending

can-not be   real.   We thank you,   day.   *rit.*

F   G7   C   Ped. sus to end.

Words and Music: Gregory Norbet, O.S.B. and
Mary David Callahan, O.S.B.

648

1. Wel-come all ye no-ble saints of old, _____ as now be-fore your ve-ry eyes un-fold _____ the won-ders all so long a-go fore-told. _____

Chorus

God and man at ta-ble are sat down, _____

God and man at ta-ble are sat down. _____

2. Elders, martyrs, all are falling down,
   prophets, patriarchs are gath'ring round;
   what angels longed to see, now man has found.

3. Who is this who spreads the vict'ry feast?
   Who is this who makes our warring cease?
   Jesus risen, Saviour, Prince of Peace.

4. Beggars, lame, and harlots also here;
   repentant publicans are drawing near;
   wayward sons come home without a fear.

5. Worship in the presence of the Lord
   with joyful songs, and hearts in one accord,
   and let our host at table be adored.

6. When at last this earth shall pass away,
   when Jesus and his bride are one to stay,
   the feast of love is just begun that day.

649 GREENSLEEVES (87.87.68.67)

1. What child is this, who, laid to rest, on Mary's lap is sleeping?
   Whom angels greet with anthems sweet, while shepherds watch are keeping?
   This, this is Christ the King,
   whom shepherds guard and angels sing:
   come greet the infant Lord, the Babe, the Son of Mary!

2. Why lies he in such mean estate, where ox and ass are feeding?
   Good Christians, fear: for sinners here the silent Word is pleading.
   Nails, spear, shall pierce him through,
   the cross be borne for me, for you:
   hail, hail the Word made flesh, the Babe, the Son of Mary!

3. So bring him incense, gold and myrrh, come peasant, king, to own him.
   The King of kings salvation brings, let loving hearts enthrone him.
   Raise, raise the song on high,
   the Virgin sings her lullaby:
   joy, joy for Christ is born, the Babe, the Son of Mary!

Words: W.C.Dix (1837-98)
Music: Traditional

Harmony for Celebration Hymnal by Steven Foster © Mayhew-McCrimmon Ltd

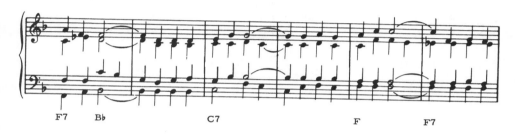

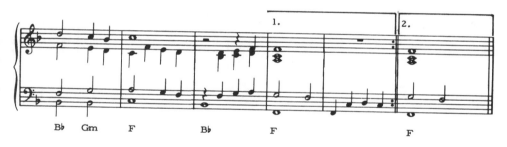

1. What do you ask of me? What would you have me do?
    I give myself within these gifts I offer you.
    This bread is food for life.
    This wine is spirit of love for you.

2. What can I offer you? You've given life to me.
    You're part of all I am. What would you have me be?
    This bread is food for life.
    This wine is spirit of love for me.

Words and music: Miriam Therese Winter

© 1971, 1980 Medical Mission Sisters, Phila., Pa.

Harmony: for Celebration Hymnal
by John Rombaut

© 1981 Mayhew-McCrimmon Ltd

651 ST VENANTIUS (88.88)

1. When Je- sus comes to be bap- tized, he leaves the

hid- den years be- hind, the years of safe- ty

and of peace, to bear the sins of all man- kind.

2. The Spirit of the Lord comes down,
   anoints the Christ to suffering,
   to preach the word, to free the bound,
   and to the mourner, comfort bring.

3. He will not quench the dying flame,
   and what is bruised he will not break,
   but heal the wound injustice dealt,
   and out of death his triumph make.

4. Our everlasting Father, praise,
   with Christ, his well-beloved Son,
   who with the Spirit reigns serene,
   untroubled trinity in One.

Words: From Stanbrook Abbey © The Benedictines of Stanbrook
Music: Rouen Church Melody
        harmonized by Stephen Dean

Arrangement © Mayhew-McCrimmon Ltd

LAUDES DOMINI (666.666)

1. When morn-ing gilds the skies, my heart a- wak- ing cries,

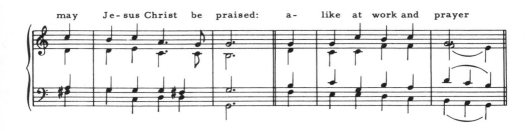

may Je-sus Christ be praised: a- like at work and prayer

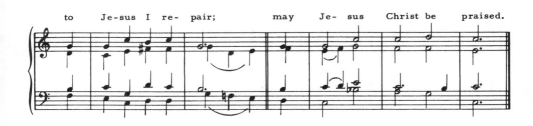

to Je-sus I re- pair; may Je- sus Christ be praised.

2. To God, the word on high
   the hosts of angels cry:
   may Jesus Christ be praised!
   Let mortals, too, upraise
   their voice in hymns of praise:
   May Jesus Christ be praised!

3. Let earth's wide circle round
   in joyful notes resound:
   May Jesus Christ be praised!
   Let air, and sea, and sky,
   from depth to height reply:
   May Jesus Christ be praised!

4. Does sadness fill my mind?
   A solace here I find,
   may Jesus Christ be praised:
   or fades my earthly bliss?
   My comfort still is this,
   may Jesus Christ be praised!

5. The night becomes as day,
   when from the earth we say,
   may Jesus Christ be praised:
   the powers of darkness fear,
   when this sweet chant they hear,
   may Jesus Christ be praised.

6. Be this, while life is mine,
   my canticle divine,
   may Jesus Christ be praised:
   be this the eternal song
   through ages all along,
   may Jesus Christ be praised.

Words: 19th century, translated by E. Caswall.
Music: Sir J. Barnby 1838-96

653

D A Bm F#m G Em A G D A7 D E7 A

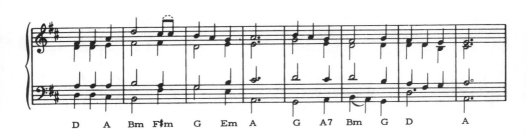

D A Bm F#m G Em A G A7 Bm G D A

A7 Cdim Em D/A A7 D

1. When the time came to stretch out his arms,
   and to lay down his life for his friends
   God's only Son in the breaking of bread,
   gave his own flesh as food for mankind,
   gave his own flesh as food for mankind.

2. This is my flesh, O take it and eat.
   This is my blood, O take it and drink,
   and to proclaim my death for mankind,
   this must you do, until I return,
   this must you do, until I return.

3. Hunger and thirst no longer we fear,
   Christ's holy flesh becomes now our food.
   And when we raise his chalice to drink,
   joy overflows, our hope is renewed,
   joy overflows, our hope is renewed.

4. O bread of life, O Banquet Divine,
   sign of the love that makes us all one.
   We who now share this gift from above,
   surely have seen the goodness of God,
   surely have seen the goodness of God.

5. Through Jesus Christ, the perfect high Priest
   and in the Spirit source of our peace.
   For this great feast which you have prepared
   Father above, O praised be your name,
   Father above, O praised be your name.

Words: Michel Scouarnec
       translated by Margaret Daly et al.
Music: Jo Akepsimas

Original French © SEFIM
English arrangement © Margaret Daly

Note: Hymn 654 will be found after No.655

1. Who wants to live as God here on this earth (2)
   must go the way of all seed,
   in doing so find mercy. (2)

2. Must go the way of all things born of earth,(2)
   must share the fate, with heart and soul,
   of all things bound for dying.

3. Both sun and rain will touch each of his days; (2)
   the smallest seed, come rain or shine,
   must die so as to live.(2)

4. So people live to die for one another,(2)
   the smallest seed, as living bread,
   to feed, sustain each other.(2)

5. And that is how our Lord and God has shown himself,(2)
   and so becomes his living self
   for each of us on earth.(2)

Music © Bernard Huijbers; Text © Huub Oosterhuis;
Translation © Tony Barr
Published by Jabulani Music Ltd, 9 Patmore Road,
Colchester, Essex

655 ECCLESIA (87.87.87.87.87.87)

Verse

Refrain

1. Who is she that stands triumphant,
   rock in strength, upon the rock,
   like some city crowned with turrets,
   braving storm and earthquake shock?
   Who is she her arms extending,
   blessing thus a world restored,
   all the anthems of creation
   lifting to creation's Lord?

   Hers the kingdom, hers the sceptre;
   fall, ye nations, at her feet;
   hers that truth whose fruit is freedom;
   light her yoke, her burden sweet.

2. As the moon its splendour borrows
   from a sun unseen at night,
   so from Christ, the sun of justice,
   evermore she draws her light.
   Touch'd by his, her hands have healing,
   bread of life, absolving key:
   Christ incarnate is her bridegroom,
   God is hers, his temple she.

3. Empires rise and sink like billows,
   vanish, and are seen no more;
   glorious as the star of morning
   she o'erlooks the wild uproar.
   Hers the household all-embracing,
   hers the vine that shadows earth:
   blest thy children, mighty mother;
   safe the stranger at thy hearth.

Words: Aubrey de Vere (1814–1902)
Music: Richard R. Terry (1865–1938)

Words © Burns & Oates Ltd

654

Note: Hymn 656 will be found after No.653

Refrain

E7   Am   E7   Am   Am7   Dm6   B7

E7   Am   E7   Am   Am7

Fine   Verse

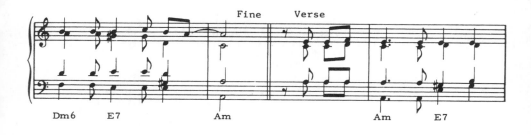

Dm6   E7   Am   Am   E7

Am   Am7   Dm   Dm6   E7

D.C.

Am   E7   Am   Am7   Dm6   E7   Am

Whey he day? Whey he day? Whey he day, mi Lard?
Whey he day? Whey he day? Whey he day, mi Lard?
Whey he day? Whey he day? Whey he day, mi Lard?
Ah cyant fine he, fine he at all.

1. Ah want to see de man from Galalee,
    Ah want to see de man who set me free,
    Ah want to see de man who die for me,
    Ah cyant fine he, fine he at all.

2. Ah want to see de man who bleed for me.
    Ah want to see de man dey scourge for me.
    Ah want to see dis man from Galalee,
    Ah cyant fine he, fine he at all.

3. Whey de man who make de bline to see?
    Whey de man who set de captive free?
    Whey de man who make de lame to walk?
    An de lil dumb boy to talk?

Words and music: Anthony Pierre
Harmony: for Celebration Hymnal
by Eric Welch

657

Wind and fire, the signs of pow'r
giv'n by God at Pentecost,
to Apostles, full of joy,
when their waiting days were past.

1. Wind, which at creation's start
   stirred dark waters into life;
   living Spirit, vital breath,
   breathing life through man and wife.

Repeat Refrain

2. Out they burst into the streets,
   stirred the people with their news;
   set explosive in men's minds
   then God's Spirit lit the fuse.

3. Hearts ablaze and free from fear,
   we'll amaze the world again,
   and God's wind and fire will still
   surge into the minds of men.

Refrain

Wind and fire, the signs of pow'r
giv'n by God to us today;
fire, to set our hearts ablaze:
wind, to blow our fears away.

Words: Alan Gaunt & John Marsh
Music: Bill Tamblyn

Words ©Alan Gaunt & John Marsh
Music ©1980 Bill Tamblyn

658

Refrain

Fine Verse

D.C. al Fine

Would you like to be happy?
Would you like to be good?
Then obey God's law of love,
obey as children should.

1. You should love the Lord your God,
   with your head and hand and heart;
   you should love the Lord your God,
   body, soul and ev'ry part.

2. When your head thinks, think with love;
   when your hand works, work with love;
   when your heart beats, beat with love;
   ev'ry part must work with love.

3. You should love the Lord your God,
   you should love him best of all.
   Love all people as yourself,
   for he made and loves them all.

Source unknown
© McLaughlin and Reilly Co

659

Chorus

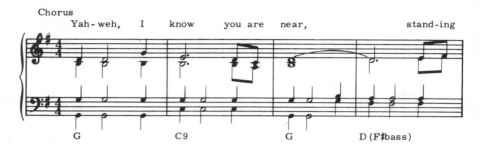

Yah-weh, I know you are near, stand-ing

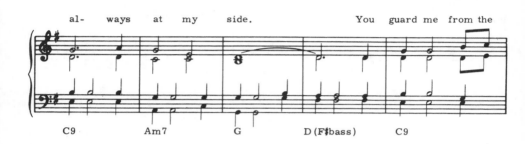

al- ways at my side. You guard me from the

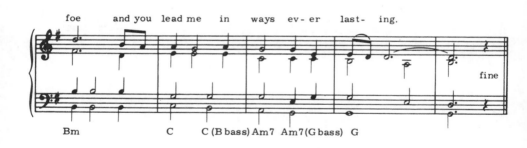

foe and you lead me in ways ev- er last- ing.

fine

1. Lord, you have searched my heart, and you know when I

sit and when I stand. Your hand is up- on me, pro-

Am   Bm   Em

tect- ing me from death, keep-ing me from harm.

Am   Bm   Am7   Am7 (G bass)   D (F♯ bass)

D.C.

2. When can I run from your love?
   If I climb to the heavens, you are there.
   If I fly to the sunrise or sail beyond the sea,
   still I'd find you there.

3. You know my heart and its ways,
   you who formed me before I was born,
   in secret of darkness, before I saw the sun,
   in my mother's womb.

4. Marvellous to me are your works;
   how profound are your thoughts, my Lord!
   Even if I could count them, they number as the stars,
   you would still be there.

Words (based on Psalm 138(139) and Music: Daniel Schutte, S.J.

660

This song should not have any harmonic accompaniment. Please resist the temptation to add 'Western' harmonies. Instead it should be accompanied by untuned percussion and spontaneous vocal harmony.

1. You, Is- ra- el re- turn now; re- turn to

God, your Fa- ther, your on- ly great cre-

a- tor; re- turn to God, your Fa- ther.

To be sung at a fast drumbeat
without pauses between verses and refrain.

2. You won't be disappointed;

3. Although you have offended;

4. Although your sins are many;

5. He's sure to listen to you;

6. For he is calling to you;

7. Now seek your Lord's forgiveness;

8. He calls you all to hear him;

9. And give yourselves to him now;

10. For he is your redeemer;

11. The people's liberator;

12. Return now, O return now;

13. You lonely and you lost ones;

14. Now pray to him his people;

15. And he will quickly answer;

16. So come now all you people;

Words: Tom Colvin
based on a Tumbuka Hymn by N.Z. Tembo
Music: Traditional Northern Malawi Melody

661

Calypso

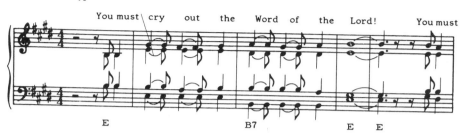

1. You must cry out the Word of the Lord!
   You must cry out the Word of the Lord!
   For you can heal a wounded man, or make a poor man rich,
   if you sing out the Word of the Lord!

2. You are called to the Word of the Lord!
   You are called to the Word of the Lord!
   For the Lord has come in power; if you believe, he lives in you,
   you must breathe out the Word of the Lord!

3. O my people, don't wait any longer!
   O my people, don't wait any longer!
   For my children are starving for my living water,
   you must cry out the Word of the Lord!

4. You must cry out the Word of the Lord!
   You must cry out the Word of the Lord!
   For you can heal a wounded man, or make a poor man rich,
   if you give out the Word of the Lord!

Words and music: Carol Gordon
Harmony: for Celebration Hymnal
by Eric Welch

1. You ser-vants of God, now give him praise: al-le-lu - ia! Sing
2. His name let us praise e-ter-nal - ly: al-le-lu - ia! Sing

out, for his goodness fills our days: al-le-lu - ia! His
praise, night and day, on land and sea: al-le-lu - ia! The

name let us praise now and al - ways: al-le-lu - ia!
Lord's name for ev - er blest will be: al-le-lu - ia!

3. Above all creation is the Lord: alleluia!
   By all may he ever be adored: alleluia!
   For God has our fallen life restored: alleluia!

4. The weak, and the poor, and all in need: alleluia!
   The Lord without fail their pray'r will heed: alleluia!
   Above others they are blest indeed: alleluia!

5. Give praise to the Father, and the Son: alleluia!
   Give praise to the Spirit, three in one: alleluia!
   Whose reign is for evermore amen: alleluia!

Words, from Psalm 112(113):
Jean-Paul Lecot;
W.R.Lawrence;
R.B.Kelly
Music: Paul Decha

663

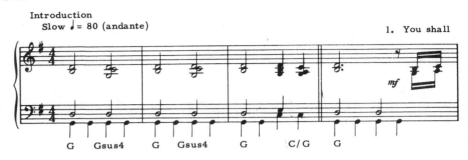

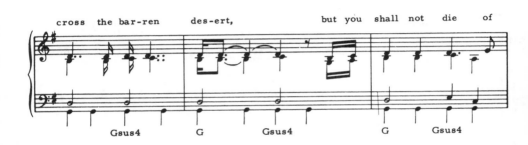

they will un- der- stand. You shall see the face of God and

C F D G E A A7

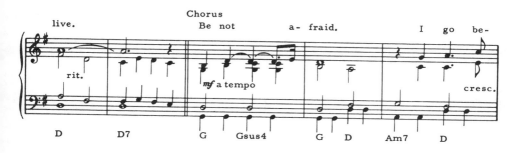

Chorus

live. Be not a- fraid. I go be-

rit. mf a tempo cresc.

D D7 G Gsus4 G D Am7 D

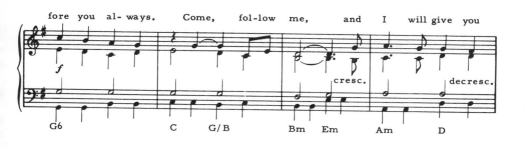

fore you al- ways. Come, fol- low me, and I will give you

f cresc. decresc.

G6 C G/B Bm Em Am D

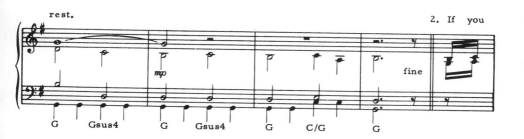

rest. 2. If you

mp fine

G Gsus4 G Gsus4 G C/G G

pass   through   ra- ging   wa- ters   in   the   sea,   you shall not

G   Gsus4   G   Gsus4   G   Gsus4

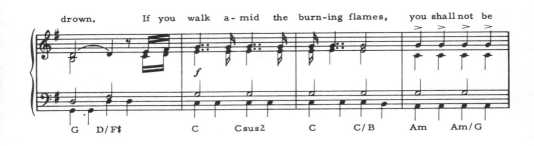

drown.   If   you   walk   a- mid   the   burn-ing flames,   you shall not be

G   D/F♯   C   Csus2   C   C/B   Am   Am/G

harmed.   If   you   stand   be-fore   the   pow'r of   hell   and   death   is   at   your

D/F♯   G   B7   Em   Am   C   F

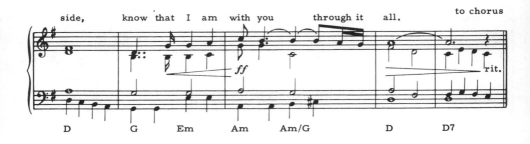

side,   know that I am with you   through it   all.   to chorus

D   G   Em   Am   Am/G   D   D7

3. Bless-ed are your poor, for the king-dom shall be theirs.

G Gsus4 G Gsus4 G Gsus4 G D/F♯

Blest are you that weep and mourn, for one day you shall laugh. And if

C Csus2 C C/B Am Am/G D/F♯

wick-ed men in-sult and hate you all be-cause of me,

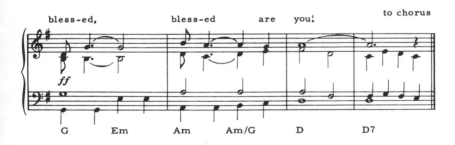

G B7 Em Am C F D

bless-ed, bless-ed are you! to chorus

G Em Am Am/G D D7

Words (based on Isaiah 43 and Luke 6) and Music: Bob Dufford, S.J.

664

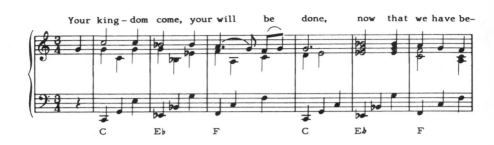

Your king-dom come, your will be done, now that we have be-

C   Eb   F   C   Eb   F

-come your sons. Let the prayer of our hearts dai-ly be:

C   Eb   F   C

'God, make us your fa - mi-ly.'   Last time to Coda   The

Eb   F   C

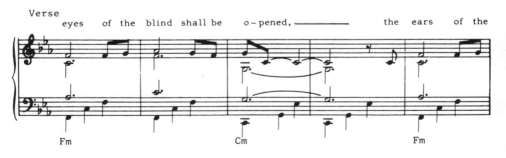

Verse
eyes of the blind shall be o-pened, ——— the ears of the

Fm   Cm   Fm

2. The ransomed of the Lord shall return,
   the islands will sing his songs at last.
   The chaff from the wheat shall be burned,
   his kingdom on earth it shall come to pass.

3. The nations will see their shame,
   the one true God will be adored.
   They turn from their fortune and shame,
   his holy mountain shall be restored.

Words: based on Isaiah 35
by Tim Whipple
Music: Tim Whipple

665 *PSALM 8*

* To follow the biblical text, Response 1 must be
sung before verse 1 and after verse 4.

Resp 1 **How great is your name, O Lord our God through all the earth!**

Resp 2 **What is mor-tal man that you care for him?**

PSALM 8

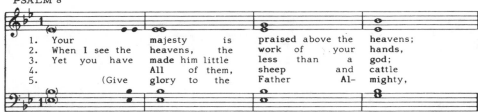

1.	Your	majesty	is	praised above the	heavens;
2.	When I see the	heavens,	the	work of your	hands,
3.	Yet you have	made him little	less	than a	god;
4.		All	of them,	sheep and	cattle
5.	(Give	glory to the	Father	Al-	mighty,

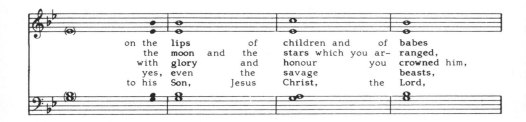

on the	lips	of	children and	of babes
the	moon and	the	stars which you ar-	ranged,
with	glory	and	honour you	crowned him,
yes, even	the	savage	beasts,	
to his	Son,	Jesus	Christ, the	Lord,

you have found **praise** to **foil** your **enemy,**
what is **man** that you should **keep** him in **mind,**
gave him **power** over the **works** of your **hand,**
birds of the **air** and **fish**
to the **Spirit** who **dwells** in our **hearts**

to **silence** the **foe** and the **rebel.**
mortal **man** that you **care** for **him?**
put **all** things under his **feet.**
that **make** their **way** through the **waters.** *
both **now** and for **ever./** **A-** **men.)**

Words: Psalm 8
Music: Psalm by Joseph Gelineau
Response 1 & 2
by A. Gregory Murray

666

Response 1

You, O Lord, have the message of e-ter-nal life.

Response 2

Your words are spi- rit, Lord, and they are life.

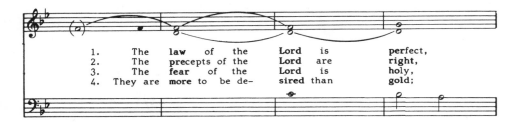

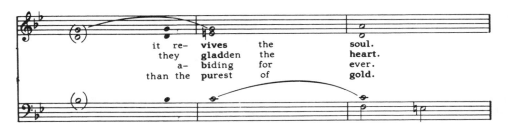

1.	The	law	of the	Lord is	perfect,
2.	The	precepts of the	Lord are	right,
3.	The	fear	of the	Lord is	holy,
4.	They are	more to be de-	sired than	gold;

it re- **vives** the **soul.**
they **gladden** the **heart.**
a- **biding** for **ever.**
than the **purest** of **gold.**

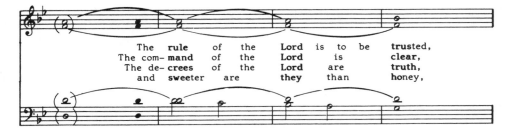

The **rule** of the **Lord** is to be **trusted,**
The com- **mand** of the **Lord** is **clear,**
The de- **crees** of the **Lord** are **truth,**
and **sweeter** are **they** than **honey,**

it gives	**wis**dom	to	the	**simple.**
it gives	**light**	to	the	**eyes.**
and	**all**	of	them	**just.**
than	**honey**	from	the	**comb.**

5. So in **them** your **serv**ant finds in in**struc**tion,
   great re**ward** is in their **keep**ing.
   But **who** can de**tect** all his **errors**?
   From **hid**den faults ac**quit** me.

6. From pre**sump**tion re**strain** your **serv**ant,
   and **let** it not **rule** me.
   Then shall I be **blame**less,
   clean from grave **sin.**

7. May the **spoken words** of my **mouth**,
   the **thoughts** of my **heart**,
   win **fav**our in your **sight**, O **Lord**,
   my **Res**cuer, my **Rock!**

8. (Praise the **Fa**ther, the **Son** and holy **Spir**it
   both **now** and for **ever**,
   the God who **is**, who **was** and who **will** be,
   world without **end.**)

Words: Psalm 18(19)

Music: Response 1 by Joseph Gelineau © 1963 The Grail (England

Response 2 © Stephen Dean

667

PSALM 22(23)

Response 1 My shep-herd is the Lord, no-thing in-deed shall I want.

Response 2 His good-ness shall fol-low me al-ways to the end of my days.

Response 3 The Lord him-self will give me re-pose.

PSALM

1.
2.   The   Lord   is   my   shepherd;
2.   He   guides me   a-   long   the   right   path;
3. You have pre- pared   a   banquet   for   me
4.   Surely goodness and   kindness shall   follow me
5.   To the Father   and   Son   give   glory,

1. there is nothing I shall **want.**
2. he is **true** to his **name.**
3. in the **sight** of my **foes.**
4. all the **days** of my **life.**
5. give **glory** to the **Spirit.**

1. **Fresh** and **green** are the **pastures**
2. If I should **walk** in the **valley** of **darkness**
3. My **head** you have a-**noin**ted with **oil;**
4. In the **Lord's** own **house** shall I **dwell**
5. To God who **is,** who **was,** and who **will** be

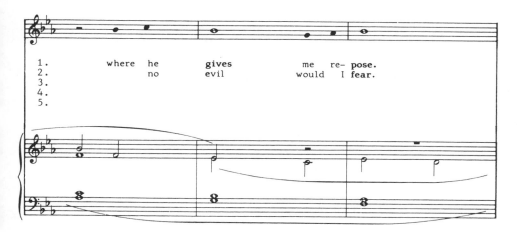

1. where he **gives** me re- **pose.**
2. no **evil** would I **fear.**
3.
4.
5.

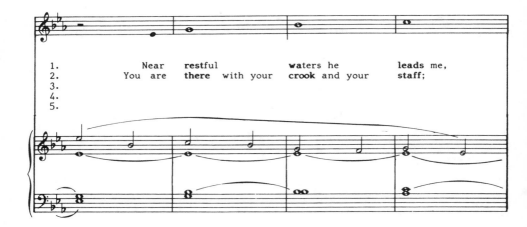

1.
2.
3.
4.
5.

1.	Near	restful	waters he	leads me,
2.	You are	**there** with your	**crook** and your	**staff;**

1.	to re–	vive	my	drooping	spi–	rit.
2.	with these	you	give me	com–	fort.
3.	my	cup	is	o – ver–	flo–	wing.
4.	for ev–	er	and	e–	ver.
5.	for ev–	er	and	e–	ver.

Words: Psalm 22
Music: Psalm and Response 1
       by Joseph Gelineau

© 1963 The Grail (England)

       Response 2 by A.Gregory Murray
       Response 3 by Robert B.Kelly

© Mayhew–McCrimmon Ltd

Response 1

Seek the face of the Lord and yearn for him.

Response 2

O–pen wide, O you gates e – ter – nal, and

let the King of glo – ry en – ter.

Response 3

Ho – san – na to the Son of Da – vid!
Ho – san – na in the highest hea – ven!

1. The Lord's is the earth and its fullness,
2. Who shall climb the mountain of the Lord?
3. He shall re–ceive blessings from the Lord.

the world and all its peoples.
Who shall stand in his ho – ly place?
and re–ward from the God who saves him.

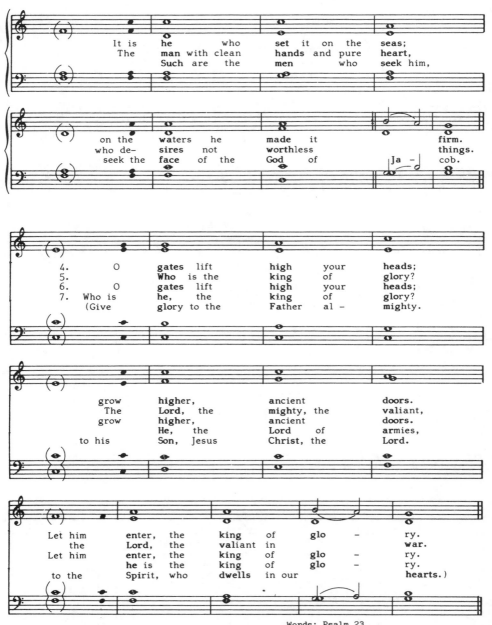

It is   he   who   set it on the seas;
The   man with clean hands and pure heart,
Such are the   men   who   seek him,

on the   waters he   made it   firm.
who de- sires not   worthless   things.
seek the face of the God   of   Ja - cob.

4.   O   gates lift   high your   heads;
5.   Who is the king of   glory?
6.   O   gates lift   high your   heads;
7. Who is he, the king of   glory?
(Give   glory to the Father al - mighty.

grow   higher,   ancient   doors.
The   Lord, the   mighty, the   valiant,
grow   higher,   ancient   doors.
He, the Lord of   armies,
to his Son, Jesus   Christ, the   Lord.

Let him   enter, the king of glo – ry.
the   Lord, the valiant in   war.
Let him enter, the king of glo – ry.
he is the king of glo – ry.
to the Spirit, who dwells in our   hearts.)

Words: Psalm 23
Music: Psalm & Response 2
by Joseph Gelineau
Response 1 by A. Gregory Murray
Response 3 by Robert B. Kelly

©1963 The Grail (England)

669

PSALM 24(25): 4–5, 6–7, 8–9, 10–11

Psalm Tone

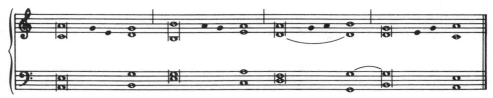

Alternative Psalm Tone

1. Lord, make me <u>know</u> your ways,
   Lord, teach <u>me</u> your paths.
   Make me wa<u>lk</u> in your <u>truth</u>, and teach me:
   for you are <u>God</u> my saviour.

2. Remember your <u>mercy</u>, Lord,
   and the love you have shown <u>from</u> of old.
   In your love re<u>member</u> me,
   because of your <u>goodness</u>, O Lord.

3. The Lord is <u>good</u> and upright.
   He shows the <u>path</u> to <u>those</u> who stray,
   he guides the humble <u>in the</u> right path;
   he teaches his way <u>to</u> the poor.

4. His ways are <u>faithfulness</u> and love
   for those who keep <u>his covenant</u> and will.
   The Lord's friendship is for those <u>who</u> revere him;
   to them he re<u>veals</u> his covenant.

5. (Glory be to the Father, and <u>to</u> the Son,
   and to the <u>Holy</u> Spirit,
   as it was in the beginning, is now, and <u>ever</u> shall be,
   world without <u>end.</u> Amen.)

Music: Response and Psalm tone by Dom Gregory Murray
       Alternative Psalm tone by Steven Foster

Words © The Grail
Music © Mayhew McCrimmon Ltd

670

PSALM 26(27)

Response 1

The Lord is my light and my help. *Fine*

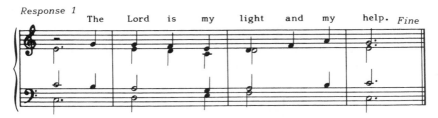

Response 2

One thing I ask of the Lord, for this I long, to

slow

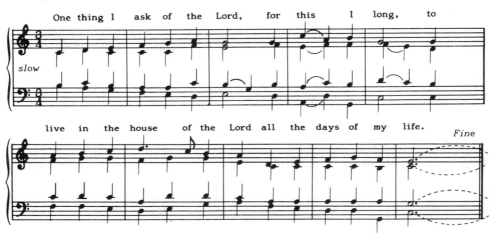

live in the house of the Lord all the days of my life. *Fine*

Response 3

I am sure I shall see the Lord's good — ness

in the land of the liv — ing. *Fine.*

Verses (Cantor, choir or all)

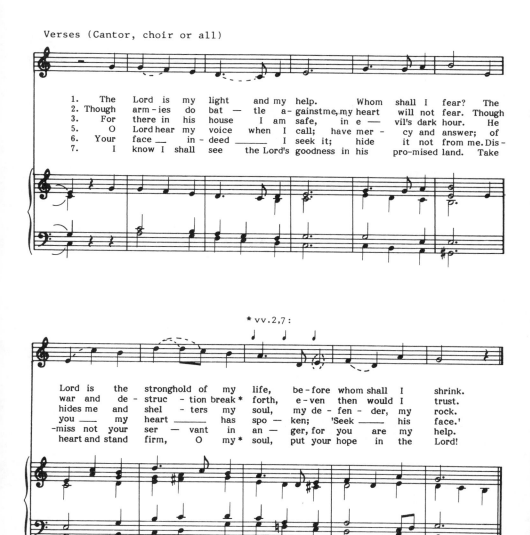

1. The Lord is my light and my help. Whom shall I fear? The
2. Though arm-ies do bat — tle a-gainst me, my heart will not fear. Though
3. For there in his house I am safe, in e — vil's dark hour. He
5. O Lord hear my voice when I call; have mer - cy and answer; of
6. Your face __ in - deed _____ I seek it; hide it not from me. Dis -
7. I know I shall see the Lord's goodness in his pro-mised land. Take

* vv.2,7 :

Lord is the stronghold of my life, be-fore whom shall I shrink.
war and de - struc - tion break * forth, e - ven then would I trust.
hides me and shel - ters my soul, my de - fen - der, my rock.
you __ my heart _____ has spo — ken; 'Seek _____ his face.'
-miss not your ser — vant in an — ger, for you are my help.
heart and stand firm, O my * soul, put your hope in the Lord!

(V.4 see over)

Words: by Stephen Dean
based on The Grail translation

Alternative (simple) setting

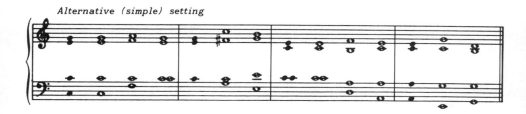

671

PSALM 41(42):1-6

Response 1

♩=○ of psalm

My soul is thirsting for the Lord; when shall I see him face to face?

Response 2

I will pour clean wa-ter o-ver you, and

cleanse you from all your sin.

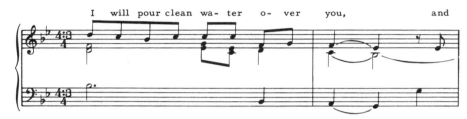

Psalm

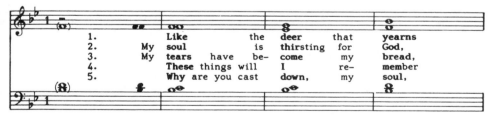

1.	Like	the	**deer** that **yearns**
2.	My	**soul** is	**thirsting** for **God**,
3.	My	**tears** have be-	**come** my **bread**,
4.		**These** things will	**I** re- **member**
5.		**Why** are you cast	**down**, my **soul**,

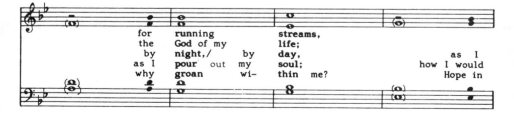

for	**running**	**streams**,
the	**God** of my	**life**;
by	**night**,/ by	**day**,
as I	**pour** out my	**soul**; as I
why	**groan** wi-	**thin** me? how I would Hope in

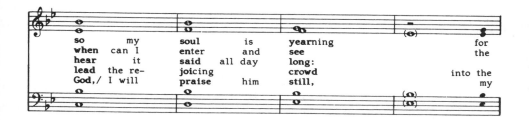

so	my	soul	is	yearning	for
when	can I	enter	and	see	the
hear	it	said	all day	long:	
lead	the re-	joicing	crowd	still,	
God,/	I will	praise	him	still,	into the

you, my God.
face of God?
'Where is your God?'
house of God.
Saviour and my God.

6. (Praise the Father, the Son, and Holy Spirit,
both now and forever,
the God who is, who was, and who will be,
world without end.)

Music: Psalm, Response 1 & 2
by Joseph Gelineau
Words: from Psalm 41

©1963 The Grail (England)

Response 1

I will go to the al-tar of God: praise the God of my joy.

Response 2

Hope in God. I will praise him still, my Sa-viour and my God.

Psalm 42

1.　　　　　De- **fend** me,　O **God** and plead my **cause**
2.　　Since **you,**　　O **God,** are my **strong**hold,
3.　　O **send** forth your **light** and your **truth,**
4. And I will **come** to the **altar** of **God,**
5.　　　**Why** are you cast **down,** my **soul,**
6. (Praise the **Father,** the **Son** and Holy **Spirit,**

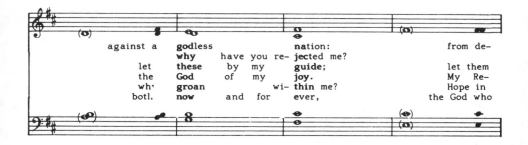

against a **godless** **nation:** from de-
　why have you re- **jected** me?
the **these** by my **guide;** let them
the **God** of my **joy.** My Re-
wh' **groan** wi- **thin** me? Hope in
botl. **now** and for **ever,** the God who

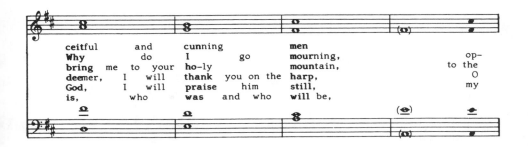

ceitful	and	cunning	men	
Why	do	**I**	go	**mourning,**	op-
bring	me to your	**ho**-ly	**mountain,**	to the
deemer,	I will	**thank** you on the	**harp,**	O
God,	I will	**praise** him	**still,**	my
is,	who	**was** and who	**will** be,	

rescue	me,	O	**God.**
pressed	by the	**foe?**
place	where you	**dwell.**
God,	my	**God.**
Saviour	and my	**God.**
world	without	**end.**)

Words: Psalm 42
Music: Psalm & Response 1
     by Joseph Gelineau
     Response 2
     by A. Gregory Murray

673

PSALM 50(51)

Have mer-cy, Lord, cleanse us from all our sin.

Response 2

Have mer-cy on us, O Lord for we have sinned.

Response 3

A pure heart cre-ate for me, O God.

1. Have mercy on me, God, in your kindness.
2. My of-fences truly I know them;
3. That you may be justified when you give sentence
4. In-deed you love truth in the heart;
5. Make me hear re-joicing and gladness,

In your com-passion blot out my of-fence.
my sin is always be-fore me.
and be with-out re-proach when you judge,
then in the secret of my heart teach me wisdom.
that the bones you have crushed may thrill.

```
1.          O    wash me more and   more    from my   guilt
2.  Against you,      you   a-     lone    have I    sinned;
3.          O    see,        in    guilt     I was   born,
4.          O    purify      me,   then I   shall be  clean;
5.  From my sins  turn      a-     way     your      face
```

```
      and cleanse    me      from      my    sin.
   what is evil            in your sight I  have  done.
        a sinner       was     I          con-  ceived.
        O wash me, I shall be whiter     than  snow.
      and blot    out      all         my    guilt.
```

6. A **pure** heart **create** for me, O **God**,
   put a **steadfast spirit within** me.
   Do not **cast me away** from your **presence**,
   nor de**prive** me of your **holy** spirit.

7. Give me a**gain** the **joy** of your **help**;
   with a **spirit** of **fervour** sus**tain** me,
   that I may **teach** trans**gressors** your **ways**,
   and **sinners** may re**turn** to **you**.

8. O **rescue** me, **God**, my **helper**,
   and my **tongue** shall **ring** out your **goodness**.
   O **Lord**, **open** my **lips**
   and my **mouth** shall de**clare** your **praise**.

9. For in **sacrifice** you **take** no **delight**,,
   burnt **offering** from **me** you would re**fuse**;
   my **sacrifice**, a **contrite spirit**.
   A **hum**bled **contrite heart** you **will** not **spurn**.

(10. Give **glory** to the Father **almighty**,
   to his **Son**, Jesus **Christ**, the **Lord**,
   to the **Spirit** who **dwells** in our **hearts**,
   both **now** and **forever**. **Amen**.)

Words: Psalm 50

Music: Psalm and Response 1 by Joseph Gelineau © 1963 The Grail (England)
   Responses 2 & 3 © Stephen Dean

PSALM 62(63) 1–6,8–9

O God you are my God, for you my soul is thirst – ing.

Psalm Tone

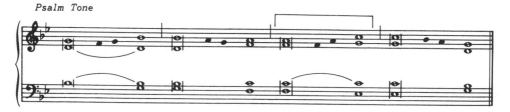

Alternative Psalm Tone

1. O God, you are my God, for <u>you</u> I long;
   for you my <u>soul</u> is thirsting.
   My body <u>pines</u> for you
   like a dry, weary land with<u>out</u> water.

2. So I gaze on you <u>in</u> the sanctuary
   to see your streng<u>th and</u> your glory.
   For your love is bet<u>ter</u> than life,
   my lips will <u>speak</u> your praise.

3. So I will bless you <u>all</u> my life,
   in your name I will lift <u>up</u> my hands.
   My mouth shall be filled as <u>with</u> a banquet,
   my mouth shall praise <u>you</u> with joy.

4. For you have <u>been</u> my help;
   in the shadow of your wings <u>I</u> rejoice.
   My soul <u>clings</u> to you;
   your right hand <u>holds</u> me fast.

5. (Glory be to the Father, and <u>to</u> the Son,
   and to the <u>Holy</u> Spirit,
   as it was in the beginning, is now, and <u>ever</u> shall be,
   world without <u>end</u>. Amen.)

675 *PSALM 83(84)*

Antiphon I

♩ = o of psalm

How love- ly is your dwell-ing place. Lord, God of hosts.

Unison only

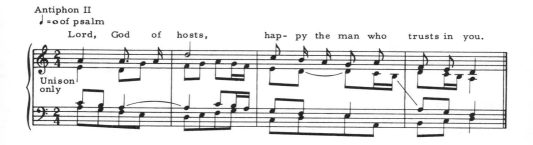

Antiphon II

♩ = o of psalm

Lord, God of hosts, hap- py the man who trusts in you.

Unison only

PSALM

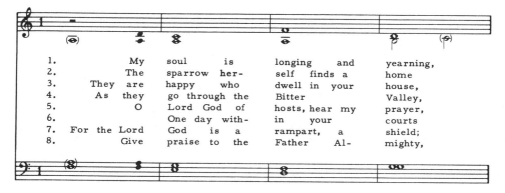

1.   My   soul   is   longing   and   yearning,
2.   The   sparrow her-   self   finds   a   home
3.   They   are   happy   who   dwell   in   your   house,
4.   As   they   go through the   Bitter   Valley,
5.   O   Lord   God   of   hosts, hear my   prayer,
6.   One day with-   in   your   courts
7. For the Lord   God   is   a   rampart,   a   shield;
8.   Give   praise   to   the   Father   Al-   mighty,

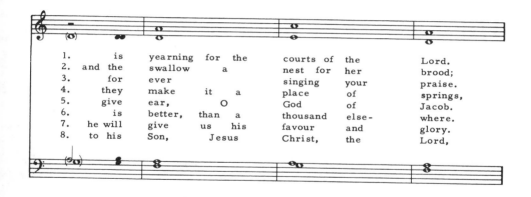

1.   is   yearning for the   courts of the   Lord.
2. and the   swallow   a   nest for her   brood;
3.   for   ever   singing   your   praise.
4.   they   make   it   a   place   of   springs,
5.   give   ear,   O   God   of   Jacob.
6.   is   better, than a   thousand else-   where.
7. he will give   us   his   favour   and   glory.
8. to his   Son,   Jesus   Christ,   the   Lord,

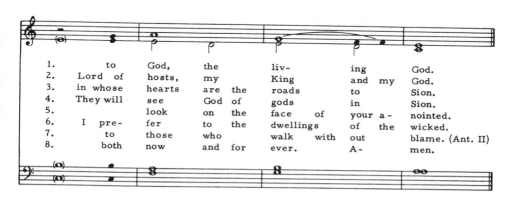

1.   My   heart and my   soul ring out their   joy
2.   she   lays   her   young   by your   altars
3. They are   happy, whose   strength is in   you,
4.   they   walk with   ever-   growing   strength.
5. Turn your eyes,   O   God,   our   shield,
6.   The threshold of the   house   of   God
7.   The Lord will not re-   fuse   any   good
8.   the Spirit who   dwells in our   hearts,

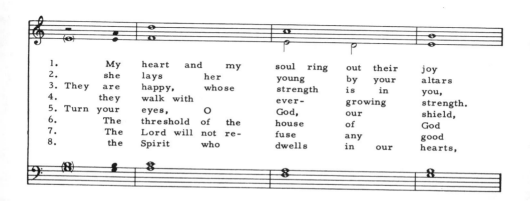

1.   to   God,   the   liv-   ing   God.
2. Lord of   hosts,   my   King   and my   God.
3. in whose hearts are the   roads   to   Sion.
4. They will see   God of   gods   in   Sion.
5.   look   on   the   face   of   your a- nointed.
6. I pre- fer   to   the   dwellings   of the   wicked.
7.   to   those   who   walk with out   blame. (Ant. II)
8.   both   now   and for   ever.   A-   men.

Words: Psalm 83

Music: Psalm by Joseph Gelineau © 1963 The Grail (England)

      Antiphons I & II by A.Gregory Murray

676 *PSALM 84(85) : 9–14*

Response 1
Let us see, O Lord your mer-cy; and give us your sa-ving help.

Response 2
Come, Lord, and save us; come, Lord, and save us.

1. I will **hear** what the Lord **God** has to **say,**
2. **Mercy** and **faithfulness** have **met;**
3. The **Lord,** will **make** us **prosper**
(4. Give **glory** to the Father al -- **mighty,**

a **voice** that **speaks** of **peace.**
justice and **peace** have em - **braced.**
and our **earth** shall **yield** its **fruit.**
to his **Son,** Jesus **Christ,** the **Lord,**

His help is **near** for **those** who **fear** him
Faithfulness shall **spring** from the **earth**
Justice shall **march** be --- **fore** him
to the **Spirit** who **dwells** in our **hearts**

and his **glory** will **dwell** in our **land.**
and **justice** look **down** from **heaven.**
and **peace** shall **follow** his **steps.**
both **now** and for **ever.** A — **men.)**

Words: Psalm 84 © 1963 The Grail (England)
Music © J.Gelineau
Harmony to Response 1 © Stephen Dean
Response 2 © Stephen Dean

677 *PSALM 90(91)*

Response 1

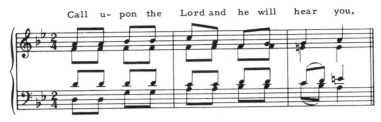

Call u-pon the Lord and he will hear you.

Response 2

Be with me, Lord, in my dis- tress!

PSALM 90

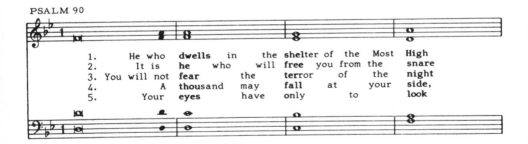

1. He who dwells in the shelter of the Most High
2. It is he who will free you from the snare
3. You will not fear the terror of the night
4. A thousand may fall at your side,
5. Your eyes have only to look

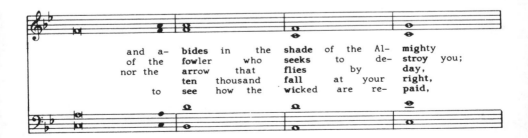

and a- bides in the shade of the Al- mighty
of the fowler who seeks to de- stroy you;
nor the arrow that flies by day,
ten thousand fall at your right,
to see how the wicked are re- paid,

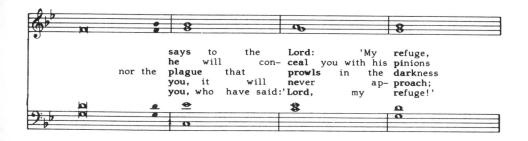

says to the Lord: 'My refuge,
he will con- ceal you with his pinions
nor the plague that prowls in the darkness
you, it will never ap- proach;
you, who have said:'Lord, my refuge!'

my stronghold, my God, in whom I trust!'
and under his wings you will find refuge
nor the scourge that lays waste at noon,
his faithfulness is buckler and shield.
and have made the Most High your dwelling.

6. Upon **you** no evil shall **fall**,
   no **plague** approach where you **dwell**.
   For **you** has he commanded his **angels**,
   to **keep** you in **all** your **ways**.

7. They shall **bear** you up**on** their **hands**
   lest you **strike** your **foot** against a **stone**.
   On the **lion** and the **viper** you will **tread**
   and **trample** the young **lion** and the **dragon**.

8. His **love** he set on **me**, so I will **rescue** him;
   protect him for he **knows** my **name**.
   When he **calls** I shall **answer**: 'I am **with** you.'
   I will **save** him in dis**tress** and give him **glory**.

9. With **length** of **life** I will content him;
   I shall **let** him see my **saving power**.
   (To the **Father**, the **Son** and Holy **Spirit**
   give **praise** for ever./ **Amen**.)

Words: Psalm 90
Music: Psalm & Response 2
    by Joseph Gelineau
    Response 1 by A. Gregory Murray

678

PSALM 92(93)

Response 1.

The Lord is King for e-ver more!

Response 2.

Al – le – lu – ia, al – le – lu – ia, al – le – lu – ia!

1. The Lord is **king** with **majesty** en– **robed;**
2. The **world** you made **firm,** not to be **moved;**
3. The **waters** have **lifted** up O **Lord,**
4. **Greater** than the **roar** of mighty **waters,**
5. **Truly,** your de– **crees** are to be **trusted.**
6. (Give **glory** to the **Father** Al– **mighty,**

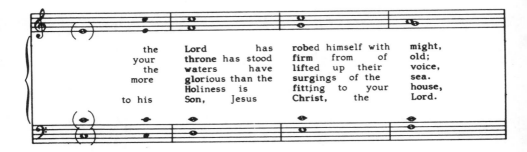

the **Lord** has **robed** himself with **might,**
your **throne** has stood **firm** from of **old;**
the **waters** have **lifted** up their **voice,**
more **glorious** than the **surgings** of the **sea.**
Holiness is **fitting** to your **house,**
to his **Son,** **Jesus** **Christ,** the **Lord.**

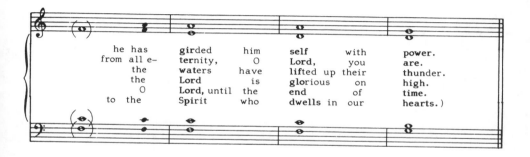

he has **gir**ded him **self** with **power.**
from all e- **ternity,** O **Lord,** you **are.**
the **waters** have **lifted** up their **thunder.**
the **Lord** is **glor**ious on **high.**
O **Lord,** until the **end** of **time.**
to the **Spirit** who **dwells** in our **hearts.**)

Words: Psalm 92
Music: Psalm — Joseph Gelineau
       Response 1 & 2 — A.Gregory Murray

679

PSALM 94 (95)

Response 1

O come let us wor-ship the Lord!

Response 2

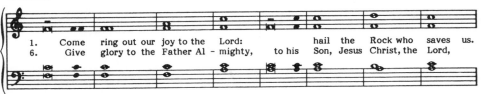

O that to-day you would lis-ten to his voice, har-den not your hearts.

PSALM

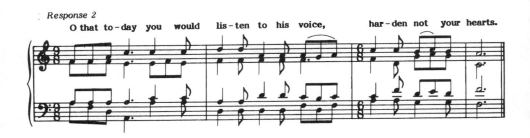

1. Come ring out our joy to the Lord: hail the Rock who saves us.
6. Give glory to the Father Al-mighty, to his Son, Jesus Christ, the Lord,

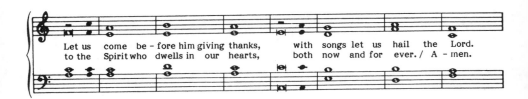

Let us come be-fore him giving thanks, with songs let us hail the Lord.
to the Spirit who dwells in our hearts, both now and for ever. / A - men.

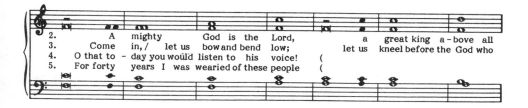

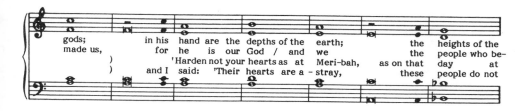

2. A mighty God is the Lord, a great king a-bove all
3. Come in, / let us bow and bend low; let us kneel before the God who
4. O that to - day you would listen to his voice! (
5. For forty years I was wearied of these people (

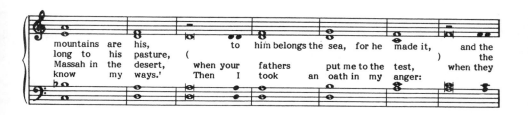

gods; in his hand are the depths of the earth; the heights of the
made us,) for he is our God / and we the people who be-
) 'Harden not your hearts as at Meri-bah, as on that day at
) and I said: 'Their hearts are a - stray, these people do not

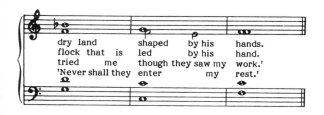

mountains are his, to him belongs the sea, for he made it, and the
long to his pasture, ( ) the
Massah in the desert, when your fathers put me to the test, when they
know my ways.' Then I took an oath in my anger:

dry land shaped by his hands.
flock that is led by his hand.
tried me though they saw my work.'
'Never shall they enter my rest.'

Words and Music: J.Gelineau © The Grail

680

Response 1

A-rise, come to your God, sing him your songs of re-joi- cing.

Response 2

Glo-ry to you, O God.

Response 3

Al-le-lu- ia, al-le-lu- ia, al-le-lu- ia.

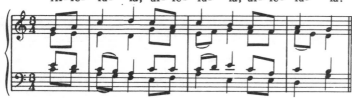

Response 4

We are his peo-ple, the sheep of his flock.

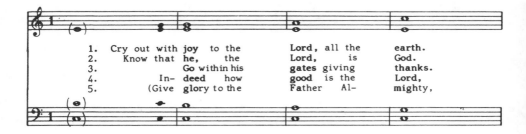

1. Cry out with **joy** to the **Lord,** all the **earth.**
2. Know that **he,** the **Lord,** is **God.**
3. **Go** within his **gates** giving **thanks.**
4. In- **deed** how **good** is the **Lord,**
5. (Give **glory** to the **Father** Al- **mighty,**

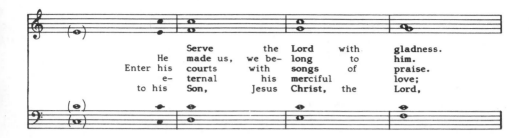

	Serve	the	Lord	with	gladness.
He	made us,	we be-	long	to	him.
Enter his	courts	with	songs	of	praise.
e-	ternal	his	merciful		love;
to his	Son,	Jesus	Christ,	the	Lord,

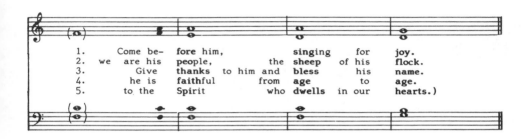

1.	Come be-	fore him,		singing	for	joy.
2.	we are his	people,	the	sheep	of his	flock.
3.	Give	thanks	to him and	bless	his	name.
4.	he is	faithful	from	age	to	age.
5.	to the	Spirit	who	dwells	in our	hearts.)

Words: Psalm 99
Music: Psalm, Response 1 & 2
        by Joseph Gelineau
        Response 3 by A. Gregory Murray
        Response 4 © Stephen Dean

681

PSALM 102(103):1-4, 8, 10, 12-13

Harmony

Resp.1. The Lord is compas-sion and love: alle - lu - ia, al - le - lu - ia!
Resp.2. The Lord has set his sway in heaven:

Unison

Psalm 102

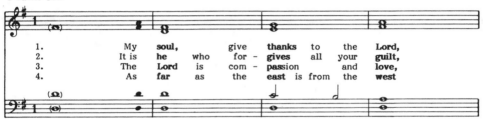

1. My soul, give thanks to the Lord,
2. It is he who for-gives all your guilt,
3. The Lord is com-passion and love,
4. As far as the east is from the west

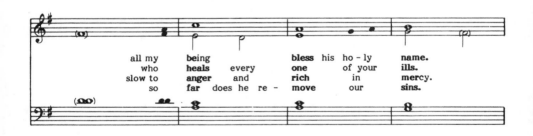

all my being bless his ho-ly name.
who heals every one of your ills.
slow to anger and rich in mercy.
so far does he re-move our sins.

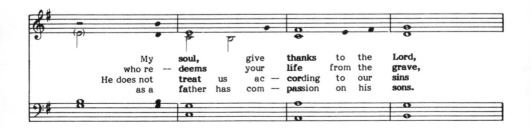

My soul, give thanks to the Lord,
who re-deems your life from the grave,
He does not treat us ac-cording to our sins
as a father has com-passion on his sons.

and   never   for   **get**   all   his   **bless**ings.
who   **crowns** you with   **love**   and com - **passion.**
nor re —   **pay**   us ac —   **cor**ding   to   our   **faults.**
the Lord has   **pity**   on   **those**   who   **fear** him.

5. (Give **glory** to the **F**ather al**might**y,
   to his **Son**, Jesus **Christ**, the **Lord,**
   to the **Spirit** who **dwells** in our **hearts**
   both **now** and for **ever./Amen.**)

Words: Psalm 102 (part)
Music: Joseph Gelineau

682

PSALM 103(104: 1–2. 5–6, 10–14, 24, 27–30)

Response Send forth your Spi – rit, O Lord and re – new the face of the earth.

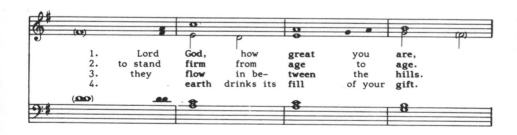

1.   **Bless** the **Lord,** my **soul!**
2. You **founded** the **earth** on its **base,**
3. You make **springs** gush **forth** in the **valleys:**
4. From your **dwelling** you **water** the **hills;**

1. Lord **God,** how **great** you **are,**
2. to stand **firm** from **age** to **age.**
3. they **flow** in be– **tween** the **hills.**
4.   **earth** drinks its **fill** of your **gift.**

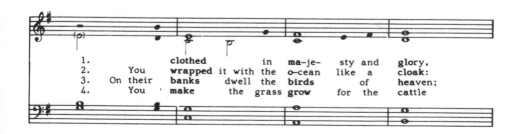

1.   **clothed** in **ma–je–** sty and **glory,**
2. You **wrapped** it with the **o–cean** like a **cloak:**
3. On their **banks** dwell the **birds** of **heaven;**
4. You **make** the grass **grow** for the **cattle**

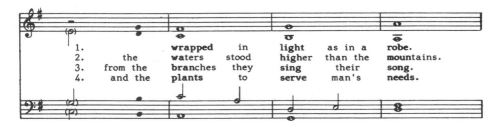

1.		wrapped	in	light	as in a	robe.
2.	the	waters	stood	higher	than the	mountains.
3.	from the	branches	they	sing	their	song.
4.	and the	plants	to	serve	man's	needs.

5. How **many** are your **works**, O **Lord**!
In **wisdom** you **made** them **all**.
The **earth** is **full** of your riches.
Bless the **Lord**, my **soul**!

6. All **creatures look** to **you**
to **give** them their **food** in due **season**.
You **give** it, they **gather** it **up**:
you **open** your **hand**, they have their **fill**.

7. You **take** back your **spirit**, they **die**,
returning to the **dust** from which they **came**.
You **send** forth your **spirit**, they are **created**;
and you **renew** the **face** of the **earth**.

8. May the **glory** of the **Lord** last for **ever**!
May the **Lord** re**joice** in his **works**!
May my **thoughts** be **pleasing** to **him**.
I **find** my **joy** in the **Lord**.

9. (Give **glory** to the **Father** al**mighty**,
to his **Son**, Jesus **Christ**, the **Lord**,
to the **Spirit** who **dwells** in our **hearts**
both **now** and for **ever**./**Amen**.)

Words : Psalm 103 (part)
translated by Joseph Gelineau/The Grail
Music : Psalm by Joseph Gelineau
Resonse by Joseph Gelineau

683 684

PSALM 114

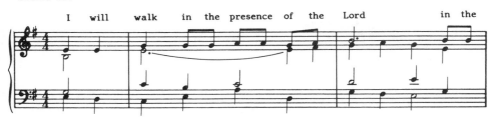

PSALM 115(116)

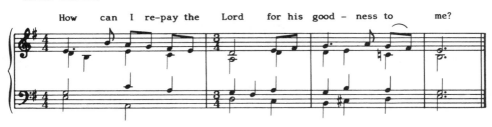

Psalm Tone

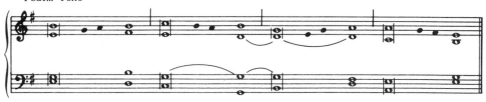

Alternative Psalm Tone

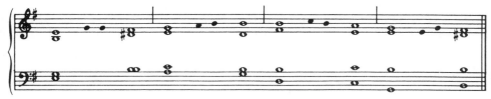

PSALM 114

1. I love the Lord for **he** has heard
   the cry of **my** appeal;
   for he turned his **ear** to me
   in the day **when** I called him.

2. They surrounded me, the snares of death,
   with the anguish **of** the tomb;
   they caught me, sorrow **and** distress.
   I called on **the** Lord's name.
   O Lord my God, deliver me!

3. How gracious is the **Lord,** and just;
   our God **has** compassion.
   The Lord protects the **simple** hearts;
   I was helpless **so** he saved me.

4. He has kept my **soul** from death,
   my eyes from tears
   and my **feet** from stumbling.
   I will walk in the presence **of** the Lord
   in the land **of** the living.

5. (Glory be to the Father, and **to** the Son,
   and to the Holy Spirit,
   as it was in the beginning, is now, and **ever** shall be,
   world without **end.** Amen.)

PSALM 115(116)

1. My vows to the Lord I **will** fulfill
   before **all** his people.
   O previous in the eyes **of** the Lord
   is the death **of** his faithful.

2. Your servant, Lord, your serv**a**nt am I;
   you have loosen**e**d my bonds.
   A thanksgiving sacr**if**ice I make:
   I will call on the Lord's name.

3. My vows to the Lord I **will** fulfill
   before **all** his people,
   in the courts of the house **of** the Lord,
   in your midst, O **J**erusalem.

4. I trusted, even **when** I said:
   'I am sore**ly** afflicted,'
   and when I said in **my** alarm:
   'No man **can** be trusted.'

5. How can I rep**ay** the Lord
   for his good**ness** to me?
   The cup of salvation I wi**ll** raise;
   I will call on the Lo**rd**'s name.

6. (Glory be to the Father, and **to** the Son,
   and to the **Hol**y Spirit,
   as it was in the beginning, is now, and **ever** shall be,
   world without **end.** Amen)

Words © The Grail

Music: First Response and Psalm-tone
        by Dom Gregory Murray
        Alternative Psalm-tone by Roger Humphrey

Music © Mayhew-McCrimmon Ltd

Second Response © by Stephen Dean

685 *PSALM 116(117)*

Cantor

All

O praise the Lord all you na – tions

Al–le–lu – ia, al–le–lu – ia! Al – le – lu – ia,

Accomp

D Am D

ac–claim him all you peo – ples!

al – le –lu – ia!

Am D Am D Em D

Strong is his love for us he is faithful for e — ver.

Am   G   D

Final coda

Al — le — lu — ia! *Repeat ad. lib.*

Am   D   Am   D

Words: Psalm 116 (Grail)
Music: Christopher Walker

Words © 1963 The Grail (England)
Music © 1979 Christopher Walker

686

PSALM 117(118):1–2, 16–17, 22–23

Response 1   *Joyfully*
Strong   rhythmic ♩. = c.60

Al - le - lu - ia,   al - le - lu - ia,   al - le - lu - ia!

Response 2   *Joyfully*

day   by

This was made the Lord;   we re - joice   and are glad.

Strong

Verse

Give thanks to the Lord   for   he   is   good, for his love

has no end. Let the sons of Is - ra-el say: 'His love

has no end, his love has no end. Al - le -

2. The Lord's right hand has triumphed;
   his right hand raised me up.
   I shall not die, I shall live
   and recount his deeds,
   recount his deeds.

3. The stone which the builders rejected
   has become the corner stone.
   This is the work of the Lord,
   a marvel in our eyes,
   a marvel in our eyes.

Words: Psalm 117/118 (part)
Music: Christopher Walker

Words © 1963 The Grail (England)
Music © Christopher Walker

687 *PSALM 121(122)*

Response 1

Give your peace, O Lord, to those who count on you.

Response 2

I re-joiced when I heard them say: Let us go to God's house!

Response 3

Let us go to God's house, re—joic——ing.

Psalm 121

1. I re- joic'd when I heard them say:
2. Je- rusalem is built as a city
3. For Israel's law it is
4. For the peace of Je- rusalem, pray:

'Let us go to God's house.
strongly com- pact.
there to praise the Lord's name
'Peace be to your homes!'

And
It is

May

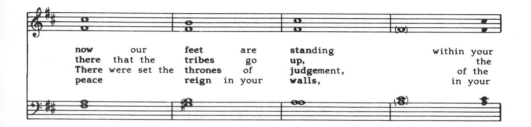

now	our	feet	are	standing		within your
there	that the	tribes	go	up,		the
There	were set the	thrones	of	judgement,		of the
peace		reign	in your	walls,		in your

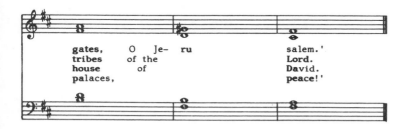

gates,	O	Je-	ru	salem.'
tribes	of the			Lord.
house	of			David.
palaces,				peace!'

5. (Praise the Father, the Son and Holy Spirit,
both now and forever,
the God who is, who was and who will be,
world without end. Amen.)

Words: Psalm 121

Music: Psalm and Response 1 by Joseph Gelineau © 1963 The Grail (England)

Response 2 & 3 © Stephen Dean

688 *PSALM 125(126)*

Antiphon I

Those who sow in tears and sor- row, one day will reap with joy.

Unison
only

Antiphon II

What mar-vels the Lord worked for us! In- deed we were glad.

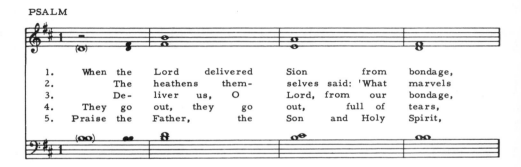

PSALM

1.	When the	Lord delivered	Sion	from bondage,
2.	The	heathens them-	selves said: 'What	marvels
3.	De-	liver us, O	Lord, from our	bondage,
4.	They go	out, they go	out, full of	tears,
5.	Praise the	Father, the	Son and Holy	Spirit,

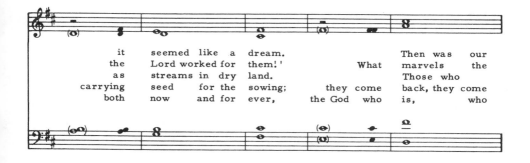

it seemed like a dream.   Then was our
the Lord worked for them!' What marvels the
as streams in dry land.   Those who
carrying seed for the sowing; they come back, they come
both now and for ever, the God who is, who

mouth filled with laughter, on our lips there were songs.
Lord worked for us! In- deed, we were glad.
sow in tears will sing when they reap.
back, full of song,   carrying their sheaves.
was and who will be,   world without end.

Words: Psalm 125

Music: Psalm and Response 1 by Joseph Gelineau © 1963 The Grail (England)

   Response 2 © by Stephen Dean

689 *PSALM 129(130)*

Response 1. I place all my trust in you my God, all my hope is in your sa- ving Word.

Response 2
With the Lord there is mer- cy and full- ness of re- demption.

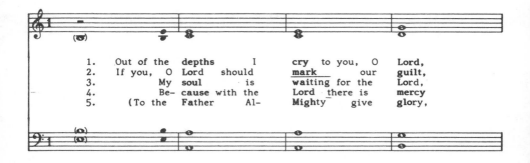

1. Out of the **depths** I **cry** to you, O **Lord,**
2. If you, O **Lord** should **mark** our **guilt,**
3. My **soul** is **waiting** for the **Lord,**
4. Be- **cause** with the **Lord** there is **mercy**
5. (To the **Father** Al- **Mighty** give **glory,**

Lord, hear my voice!
Lord, who would sur- vive?
I count on his word:
and fullness of re- demption,
give glory to his Son.

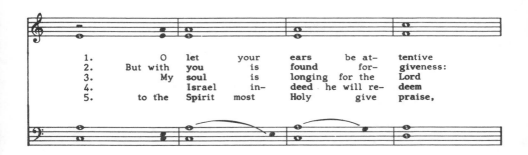

1.   O let your ears be at- tentive
2. But with you is found for- giveness:
3. My soul is longing for the Lord
4. Israel in- deed he will re- deem
5. to the Spirit most Holy give praise,

to the voice of my plea- ding.
for this we re- vere you.
more than watch- man for day- break.
from all its i- ni- quity.
whose reign is for e- ver.)

Words: *Psalm 129*
Music: *Response 1 by Joseph Gelineau c 1963 The Grail (England)*
Response 2 c by Stephen Dean

690

Voice

1. O give thanks to the Lord for he is good,
2. Who a- lone has wrought mar - vell-ous works,
3. It was he who made the great lights,
4. The first- born of the E - gyp - tians he smote
5. He di- vided the Red Sea in two,
6. Through the desert his peo - ple he led
7. He let Israel in - her - it their land,
8. And he snatched us a- way from our foes,

Great is his love, love wi - thout end.

1. give thanks to the God of gods,
2. whose wisdom it was made the skies,
3. the sun to rule in the day,
4. he brought Israel out from their midst,
5. he made Israel pass through the midst,
6. nations in their great - ness he struck,
7. on his servant their land he be - stowed,
8. he gives food to all liv- ing things,

Great is his love, love wi-thout end.

1. give thanks to the Lord of Lords.
2. who spread the earth on the seas.
3. the moon and stars in the night.
4. arm out-stretched, with power in his hand.
5. flung Pharaoh and his force in the sea.
6. kings in their splen-dour he slew.
7. he re-membered us in our dis-tress.
8. to the God of hea-ven give thanks.

Great is his love, love wi-thout end.

Words: Psalm 135
Music: Joseph Gelineau

691 *PSALM 144(145) 1–2,8–18*

I will bless your name for e – ver, O God my King.

Dom Gregory Murray

or

You o-pen wide your hand; O Lord, you grant our de – sires.

Eric Welch

Psalm Tone

Dom Gregory Murray

Alternative Psalm Tone

John Harper

1. I will give you glory, O God my King.
   I will bless your name for ever.
   I will bless you day after day
   and praise your name for ever.

2. The Lord is kind and full of compassion,
   slow to anger, abounding in love.
   How good is the Lord to all,
   compassionate to all his creatures.

3. All your creatures shall thank you, O Lord,
   and your friends shall repeat their blessing.
   They shall speak of the glory of your reign
   and declare your might, O God.

4. To make known to men your mighty deeds
   and the glorious splendour of your reign.
   Yours is an everlasting kingdom;
   your rule lasts from age to age.

5. The Lord is faithful in all his words
   and loving in all his deeds.
   The Lord supports all who fall
   and raises all who are bowed down.

6. The eyes of all creatures look to you
   and you give them their food in due time.
   You open wide your hand,
   grant the desires of all who live.

7. The Lord is just in all his ways
   and loving in all his deeds.
   He is close to all who call him,
   who call on him from their hearts.

8. (Glory be to the Father, and to the Son,
   and to the Holy Spirit,
   as it was in the beginning is now, and ever shall be, |
   world without end. Amen.)

Words © The Grail

Music: Response and Psalm-tone by Dom Gregory Murray
       Second response by Eric Welch
       Alternative Psalm-tone by John Harper

Music © Mayhew-McCrimmon Ltd

692 *PSALM 150*

al‑le‑lu ‑ ia.

2. Praise him with the blast of trumpet;
   praise him now with lyre and harps;
   praise him with the timbrel and dance;\
   praise him with the sound of string and reed.

3. Praise him with resounding cymbals;
   with cymbals that crash give praise;
   O let everything that has breath,
   let all living creatures praise the Lord.

4. Praise God the almighty Father;
   praise Christ his beloved Son;
   give praise to the Spirit of Love,
   for ever the triune God be praised.

Words: Psalm 150
       paraphrased by Omer Westendorf
Music: Jan Vermulst

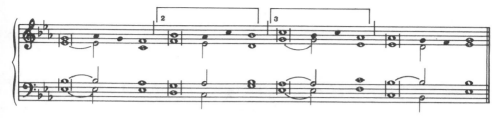

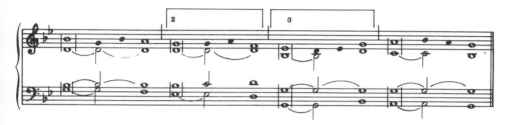

Blessed be the Lord, the God of Israel!
He has visited his people and redeemed them.　　　　... *omit sections 2 & 3 of chant*

He has raised up for us a mighty saviour
in the house of David his servant,
as he promised by the lips of holy men,
those who were his prophets from of old.

A saviour who would free us from our foes,
from the hands of all who hate us.
So his love for our fathers is fulfilled
and his holy covenant remembered.

He swore to Abraham our father to grant us,
that free from fear, and saved from the hands of our foes,
we might serve him in holiness and justice
all the days of our life in his presence.

As for you, little child,
you shall be called a prophet of God, the Most High.
You shall go ahead of the Lord
to prepare his ways before him.

To make known to his people their salvation
through forgiveness of all their sins,
the loving-kindness of the heart of our God
who visits us like the dawn from on high.

He will give light to those in darkness
those who dwell in the shadow of death,
and guide us into the way of peace.　　　　... *omit section 3 of chant*

Glory be to the Father, and to the Son,
and to the Holy Spirit,
as it was in the beginning, is now and ever shall be,
world without end, Amen.

Music: Chant 1 John Harper
　　　　 Chant 2 Steven Foster

© 1984 Mayhew-McCrimmon Ltd

694

Antiphon   THE MAGNIFICAT

♩ = ○ of canticle

The Lord has done mar- vels for me: ho- ly is his name.

is his

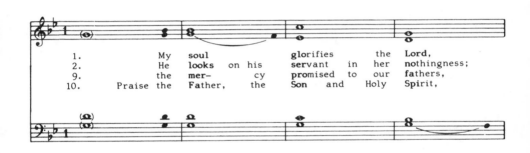

1.   My   soul   glorifies   the   Lord,
2.   He   looks   on his   servant   in   her   nothingness;
9.   the   mer–   cy   promised   to   our   fathers,
10.   Praise the   Father,   the   Son   and   Holy   Spirit,

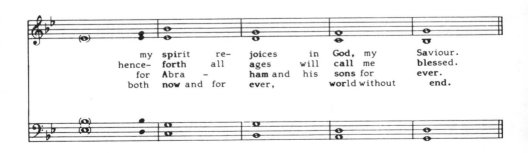

my   spirit   re–   joices   in   God, my   Saviour.
hence– forth   all   ages   will   call me   blessed.
for   Abra   –   ham and   his   sons for   ever.
both   now and for   ever,   world without   end.

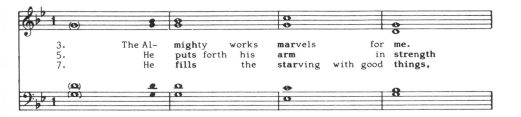

3. The Al— mighty works marvels for me.
5. He puts forth his arm in strength
7. He fills the starving with good things,

Holy his name!
and scatters the proud- hearted.
sends the rich away empty.

4. His mercy is from age to
6. He casts the mighty from their
8. He pro— tects Israel his

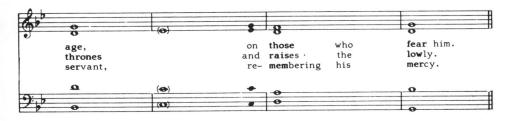

age, on those who fear him.
thrones and raises · the lowly.
servant, re- membering his mercy.

Words: Luke 1:46b-55
Music: Psalm by Joseph Gelineau
Response by A. Gregory Murray

©1963 The Grail (England)

695

THE NUNC DIMITTIS

Response 1

Guard us O Lord, while we sleep and keep us in peace.

Response 2

My eyes have seen your sal-va-tion: the light of all peo-ples.

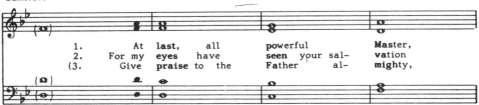

Canticle

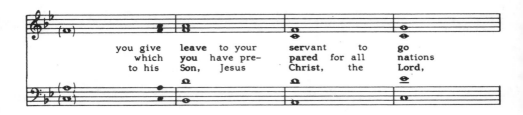

1. At last, all powerful Master,
2. For my eyes have seen your sal-vation
(3. Give praise to the Father al-mighty,

you give leave to your servant to go
which you have pre-pared for all nations
to his Son, Jesus Christ, the Lord,

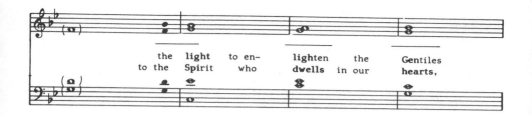

the light to en-   lighten   the   Gentiles
to the Spirit who   dwells   in our   hearts,

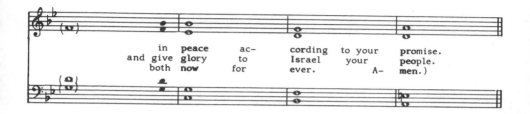

in   peace   ac-   cording   to your   promise.
and give glory   to   Israel   your   people.
both now   for   ever.   A-   men.)

Words: Canticle of Simeon from
       Luke 2:29-32 (Grail translation)
Music: Canticle and Response 2
       by Joseph Gelineau
       Response 1 by Guy Wetz

696

Equal Voices

♩=56

A Verse - CANTOR   B Refrain - ALL

(hum)   A- do- ra- mus te Do- mi- ne.

Mixed Voices

A   B

(hum)   A- do- ra- mus te Do- mi- ne.

ALTERNATE REFRAINS

Equal Voices   Mixed Voices

B   3   B   3

Lord, we wor- ship you.   Lord, we wor- ship you.

Equal Voices

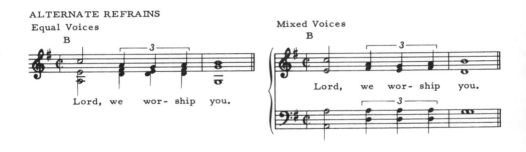

B >

Glo- ri- a!   Glo- ri- a!   Glo- ri- a!

Mixed Voices

B >

Glo- ri- a,   glo- ri- a,   glo- ri- a!

Verses

CANTOR

1. With the an-gels and arch-an-gels: 2. With the

pa-tri-archs and pro-phets: 3. With the Vir-gin Ma-ry

moth-er of God: 4. With the A- pos-tles and e- van-gel-ists:

5. With all the martyrs of Christ: 6. With all who

wit-ness to the Gos-pel of the Lord: 7. With all your

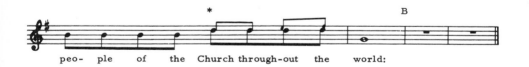

peo- ple of the Church through-out the world:

* Choose either part.

Music: Jacques Berthier

697

Music: Christopher Walker

© Christopher Walker

698

Music: William Boyce (1707-79)

Cantor

1.   Blest   the   poor   in   spirit,
2.   Blest   the   gentle,
3.   Blest those who mourn,
4. Blest those who hun-ger and   thirst   for   jus - tice,
5.   Blest   the   mer - ci - ful
6.   Blest   the   pure   in   heart,
7.   Blest   the   peacemakers
8. Blest those who suf - fer for   righteousness,   for

BLES - SED ARE THEY WHO FOL - LOW GOD'S LAW AND

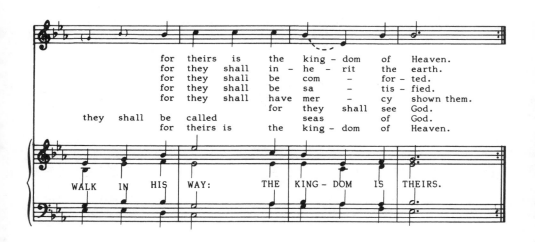

         for   theirs   is   the   king - dom   of   Heaven.
         for   they   shall   in - he - rit   the   earth.
         for   they   shall   be   com -   for - ted.
         for   they   shall   be   sa -   tis - fied.
         for   they   shall   have   mer -   cy   shown them.
                         for   they   shall   see   God.
they   shall   be   called   seas   of   God.
         for   theirs is   the   king - dom   of   Heaven.

WALK IN HIS WAY: THE KING - DOM IS THEIRS.

The chorus is sung continuously. The cantor sings verses as required.
When the cantor is singing, the people hum with closed lips.

Words from Scripture: Mt 3.5–10
Music: Stephen Dean

©1984 Stephen Dean

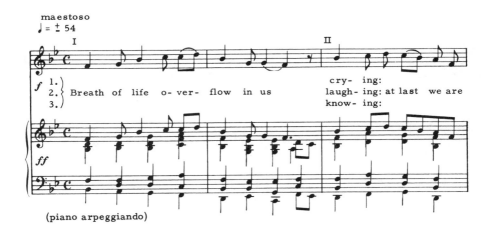

maestoso
♩ = ± 54

Breath of life o- ver- flow in us laugh- ing: at last we are cry- ing:

know- ing:

(piano arpeggiando)

born a- gain.

Performance: the three verses could be sung throughout in
unison before they are sung as a canon.

701

Do- na nobis pa- cem, pa- cem,
Do- na nobis pa- cem,
Do- na nobis pa- cem,

Do- na nobis pa- cem.
Do- na nobis pa- cem.
Do- na nobis pa- cem.

Words and music: Anonymous

702

Glo – ry be to God the Fa – ther, God the Fa – ther,

God the Son and Ho – ly Spi – rit, Ho – ly Spi – rit,

as it was and shall be e – ver – more.

703

Go out to the whole world, pro – claim the Good News.

Words: Mark 16:15

Music © 1975 Bill Tamblyn

704

I re – joiced when I heard them say, 'Let us go to God's

house.' Al – le – lu – ia!

Words: Psalm 121:1

Music © 1975 Bill Tamblyn

705

This is a simple Christmas song suitable for children. It can be sung as a round: the second voice entering when the first voice has reached the asterisk ✳ .

Je-sus Christ little Lord, God and Sa-viour he, born in-to this sin-ful world to set the peo-ple free. Je - sus come to us and teach us how to pray, we will share your joy and love and peace this Christ-mas day.

Music and Words by Roger Humphrey   © 1984 Mayhew-McCrimmon Ltd

706

Canon (Praetorius)

Ju – bi – la – te De – o, Ju – bi – la – te De – o, Al – le – lu – ia.

Accompaniments (Jaques Berthier)

(Fine)

Guita.

Choir

Ju – bi – la – te De – o,

Ju – bi – la – te, Ju – bi – la – te, Ju – bi – la – te,

Ju – bi – la – te De – o, Ju – bi – la – te,

Ju – bi – la – te, A – men.

707

Canon – (2 Voices)

Ju – bi – la – te De – o   om – nis ter – ra.   Ser – vi – te

Do – mi – no in lae – ti – ti – a.   Al – le – lu – ia, al – le – lu – ia, on lae – ti – ti –

D.C.

a.   Al – le – lu – ia, al – le – lu – ia, in lae – ti – ti – a!

Accompaniments

Keyboard or Instruments

Guitar

Music: Jacques Berthier

Let us go forth in – to the world

with the good news, spread–ing his word, for we're

Eas – ter peo – ple, saved by Christ.

Words and Music: Estelle White
© Mayhew McCrimmon Ltd

709

OSTINATO RESPONSE

All Two or three Equal Voices

♩ = 72 Two Voices:

p Mi- se- ri- cor- di- as Do- mi- ni in ae- ter- num can- ta- bo.

Third Voice ad lib.:

p

ACCOMPANIMENTS

Keyboard or Instruments

Guitar - Arpeggiated

Dm   A   Dm   C   F   C   Dm A Dm

Choir

1. *p* (hum)

2. (hum)

p

p

Verses

1. From age to age through all gen- er- a-tions, my mouth shall proclaim your

truth O Lord. 2. Who, O God, who in the u-ni-verse can compare with you?

3. Blest be the Lord for ev- er, through-out e- ter- ni- ty.

A- men! A- men!

* Choose either part.

710

711

Principal Canon

Os-ten-de no-bis Do-mi - ne, mi-se-ri - cor-di-am tu -

am. A - men! A - men! Ma-ra-na - tha! Ma-ra-na - tha! Os-ten-de. -tha.

Accompaniments

Keyboard

Guitar

Choral Accompaniment I

A men! A - men! A - men!

A - men! A - men! A - men!

Secondary Canon (or Choral Accompaniment II) Basses and Altos

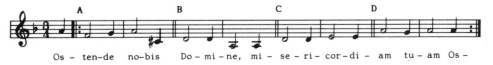

Os - ten-de no-bis Do-mi - ne, mi-se-ri-cor-di - am tu-am Os -

Choral Accompaniment III

Os — ten — de — no — bis, no — bis Do — mi — ne, mi — se — ri-

cor-di —am tu — am, tu — am, tu am. Os — am.

(mi—se—ri — cor—di — am)

1, 2, 3 . . . .

(Fine)

Music: Jacques Berthier

712

Introduction

Words and music: Linda Stassen

Harmony: for Celebration Hymnal
      by Frances M. & Robert B. Kelly

(This may be sung as a round;
successive entries are numbered)

For recorders, for flutes (8va), or tuned percussion:

Repeat as necessary

ORGAN

Repeat as necessary

Words and music: Herman Stern

©Verlag Merseburger Berlin GmbH

Harmony: for Celebration Hymnal
by Frances M. & Robert B. Kelly

©1981 Mayhew–McCrimmon Ltd

714

Stand and stare not at what used to be
and re- main not in the past. For
I, says he, make new be- gin- nings. Look,
all things are new now, do you not see?

(let each line play itself out)

Accompaniment

fine

Music c Bernard Huijbers. Text c Huub Oosterhuis. Translation c Tony Barr.
Published by Jabulani Music Ltd, 9 Patmore Road, Colchester, Essex.

715

Plainchant, arranged by Laurence Bevenot, OSB.

Arrangement © Laurence Bevenot, OSB.

716

1. Pan-ge lin-gua glo-ri-o-si Cor-po-ris mys-te-ri-um, San-guin-is que pre-ti-o-si Quem in mun-di pre-ti-um Fruc-tus ven-tris ge-ne-ro-si Rex ef-fu-dit gen-ti-um.

(after last verse)

A-men.

2. Nobis datus, nobis natus
   ex intactus Virgine;
   et in mundo conversatus,
   sparso verbi semine,
   sui moras incolatus
   miro clausit ordine.

3. In supremae nocte coenae
   recumbens cum fratribus,
   observata lege plene
   cibis in legalibus:
   cibum turbae duodenae
   se dat suis manibus.

4. Verbum caro, panem verum
   Verbo carnem efficit:
   fitque sanguis Christi merum;
   et si sensus deficit,
   ad firmandum cor sincerum
   sola fides sufficit.

5. Tantum ergo Sacramentum
   veneremur cernui;
   et antiquum documentum
   novo cedat ritui:
   praestet fides supplementum
   sensuum defectui.

6. Genitori, genitoque
   laus, et jubilatio,
   salus, honor, virtus quoque
   sit et benedictio:
   procedenti ab utroque
   compar sit laudatio. Amen.

Words: St Thomas Aquinas (1227-74)
Music: Plainchant
       arranged by Dom Gregory Murray

Arrangement © Mayhew McCrimmon Ltd

717

Words and Music: Anonymous
Music arrangement: James O'Donnell

718

ad nos con- ver- te. Et Je- sum, be- ne- di- ctum fru- ctum

ven- tris tu- i, no- bis post hoc ex- si- li- um os- ten- de.

O cle- mens, O pi- a, O-

dul- cis Vir- go Ma- ri- a.

Words and Music: Anonymous
Music Arrangement: James O'Donnell

© Mayhew McCrimmon Ltd.

719 TE DEUM LAUDAMUS

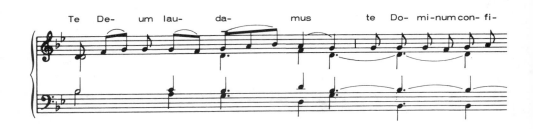

Te De- um lau- da- mus te Do- mi-num con- fi-

te- mur. Te æ- ter-num Pa- trem om- nis ter- ra ve- ne-

ra- tur. Ti- bi om- nes An- ge- li, ti- bi Cæ- li

et u- ni- ver- sæ Po- te- sta- tes. Ti- bi Che- ru- bim et

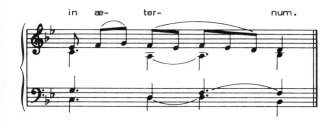

Words: Anonymous
Music: Plain Chant

Arrangement © Mayhew McCrimmon Ltd

720

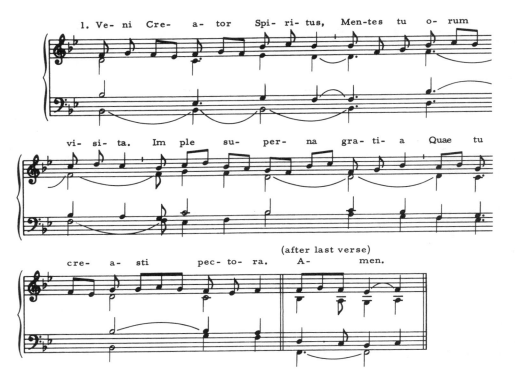

1. Ve- ni Cre- a- tor Spi- ri- tus, Men-tes tu o- rum vi- si- ta. Im ple su- per- na gra- ti- a Quae tu cre- a- sti pec- to- ra. A- men.

(after last verse)

2. Qui diceris Paraclitus,
altissimi donum Dei,
fons vivus, ignis, caritas
et spiritalis unctio.

3. Tu septiformis munere,
digitus paternae dexterae,
tu rite promissum Patris
sermone ditans guttura.

4. Accende lumen sensibus,
infunde amorem cordibus,
infirma nostri corporis
virtute firmans perpeti.

5. Hostem repellas longius
pacemque dones protinus;
ductore sic te praevio
vitemus omne noxium.

6. Per te sciamus da Patrem
noscamus atque Filium,
teque utriusque Spiritum
credamus omni tempore.
Amen.

Words: Anonymous, 9th century
Music: Plainchant, arranged by
Gregory Murray, OSB.

721

Vi – cti – mae pas – cha – li lau – des * im – mo – lent Chri – sti – a – ni.

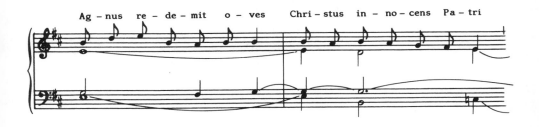

Ag – nus re – de – mit o – ves Chri – stus in – no – cens Pa – tri

re – con – ci – li – a – vit pec – ca – to – res. Mors et vi – ta du – el – lo

con – fli – xe – re mi – ran – do: dux vi tae mor – tu – us re – gnat vi – vus.

Dic no - bis Ma - ri - a, quid vi - di - sti in vi - a?

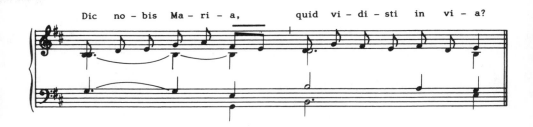

Se - pul - chrum Christi vi - ven - tis, et glo - ri - am vi - di re - sur - gen - tis:

An - ge - li - cos tes - tes, su - da - ri - um et ves - tes.

Sur - re - xit Christus spes me - a: prae - ce - det su - os in Ga - li - lae - am.

Sci – mus Chri –stum sur – re – xis – se   a   mor – tu – is ve – re:

tu   no – bis, vi –ctor Rex, mi – se – re – re.   A – men.

(At Mass only:)
(Al – le – lu – ia.)

Words: attributed to Wipo of Burgundy, 10th Century
Music: Plain chant arranged by James O'Donnell

Arrangement © 1984 Mayhew—McCrimmon Ltd

The Divine Office

The basic order of Morning and Evening Prayer is as follows:

INTRODUCTION
HYMN
PSALMODY (including a biblical canticle)
SCRIPTURE
RESPONSORY
GOSPEL CANTICLE
INTERCESSIONS AND PRAYER
BLESSING

The full texts will be found in the books containing the Divine Office. A selection is given here which will allow a parish or group to celebrate a form of morning, evening or night prayer according to their needs.

1. INTRODUCTION

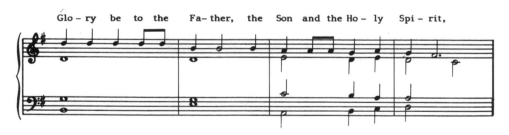

shall be   world without end, A – men,   Al – le – lu –   ia.

Except in Lent

Alternative introductions

I rejoiced when I heard them say (687)
Jubilate Deo (706)
Jubilate Deo omnis terra (707)

2. HYMN

A hymn may be chosen from any appropriate section of the book.

3. PSALMODY

First given below are the psalms used in the four-week cycle of Sunday Evening Prayer. (The Antiphons to the Psalms are not given.) Following is a list of all the psalms contained in the book. One of the items in the psalmody is usually a Canticle; these are listed after the Psalms.

Psalm 109(110)   Weeks 1–4   © Stephen Dean

1. The Lord's revelation to my Master:
   'Sit on my right:
   your foes I will put beneath your feet.'

2. The Lord will wield from Sion your sceptre of power:
   rule in the midst of all your foes.

3. A prince from the day of your birth
   on the holy mountains;
   from the womb before the dawn I begot you.

4. The Lord has sworn an oath he will not change.
   'You are a priest for ever,
   a priest like Melchizedek of old.'

5. The master standing at your right hand
   will shatter kings in the day of his wrath.

6. He shall drink from the stream by the wayside
   and therefore he shall lift up his head.

7. Glory be to the Father, and to the Son
   and to the Holy Spirit.

8. As it was in the beginning, is now, and ever shall be,
   world without end, Amen.

Psalm 113A(114)   Week 1

© Stephen Dean

1. When Israel came forth from Egypt,
   Jacob's sons from an alien people,
   Judah became the Lord's temple,
   Israel became his kingdom.

2. The sea fled at the sight:
   the Jordan turned back on its course,
   the mountains leapt like rams
   and the hills like yearling sheep.

3. Why was it sea, that you fled,
   that you turned back, Jordan, on your course?
   Mountains, that you leapt like rams,
   hills, like yearling sheep?

4. Tremble, O earth, before the Lord,
   in the presence of the God of Jacob,
   who turns the rock into a pool
   and flint into a spring of water.

5. Glory be to the Father, and to the Son
   and to the Holy Spirit,
   as it was in the beginning, is now and ever shall be,
   world without end. Amen.

Psalm 113B(115)   Week 2

Ian Forrester
©*McCrimmon Publishing Co Ltd*

1. Not to us, Lord, not to us,
   but to your name give the glory
   for the sake of your love and your truth,
   lest the heathen say: 'Where is their God?'

2. But our God is in the heavens;
   he does whatever he wills.
   Their idols are silver and gold,
   the work of human hands.

3. They have mouths but they cannot speak;
   they have eyes but they cannot see;
   they have ears but they cannot hear;
   they have nostrils but they cannot smell.

4. With their hands they cannot feel;|
   with their feet they cannot walk.
   No sound comes from their throats.
   Their makers will come to be like them,
   and so will all who trust in them.

Steven Foster
©*McCrimmon Publishing Co Ltd*

5. Sons of Israel, trust in the Lord;
   he is their help and their shield.
   Sons of Aaron, trust in the Lord;
   he is their help and their shield.

6. You who fear him, trust in the Lord;
   he is their help and their shield.
   He remembers us, and he will bless us:
   he will bless the sons of Israel|.
   He will bless the sons of Aaron.

7. The Lord will bless those who fear him,
   the little no less than the great:
   to you may the Lord grant increase,
   to you and all your children.

8. May you be blessed by the Lord
   the maker of heaven and earth.
   The heavens belong to the Lord
   but the earth has given to men.

9. The dead shall not praise the Lord,
   nor those who go down into the silence.
   But we who live bless the Lord
   now and for ever. Amen.

10. Glory be to the Father, and to the Son
    and to the Holy Spirit,
    as it was in the beginning, is now| and ever shall be
    world without end. Amen.

Psalm 110(111)   Week 3

Ian Forrester
©McCrimmon Publishing Co Ltd

Alternative Chant

Graham Elliott
©*McCrimmon Publishing Co Ltd*

1. I will thank the Lord with all my heart
   in the meeting of the just and their assembly.
   Great are the works of the Lord;
   to be pondered by all who love them.

2. Majestic and glorious his work,
   his justice stands firm for ever.
   He makes us remember his wonders.
   The Lord is compassion and love.

3. He gives food to those who fear him;
   keeps his covenant ever in mind.
   He has shown his might to his people
   by giving them the lands of the nations.

4. His works are justice and truth:
   his precepts are all of them sure,
   standing firm for ever and ever:
   they are made in uprightness and truth.

5. He has sent deliverance to his people|
   and established his covenant for ever.
   Holy his name, to be feared.
   To fear the lord is the first stage of wisdom;|
   all who do so prove themselves wise.
   His praise shall last for ever!

6. Glory be to the Father, and to the Son,
   and to the Holy Spirit,
   as it was in the beginning, is now| and ever shall be,
   world without end. Amen.

Psalm 111(112)   Week 4

John Harper
© McCrimmon Publishing Co Ltd

Alternative Chant

John Harper
© McCrimmon Publishing Co Ltd

1. Happy the man who fears the Lord,
   who takes delight in all his commands.
   His sons will be powerful on earth;
   the children of the upright are blessed.

2. Riches and wealth are in his house;
   his justice stands firm for ever.
   He is a light in the darkness for the upright:
   he is generous, merciful and just.

3. The good man takes pity and lends,
   he conducts his affairs with honour.
   The just man will never waver:
   he will be remembered for ever.

4. He has no fear of evil news;
   with a firm heart he trusts in the Lord.
   With a steadfast heart he will not fear;
   he will see the downfall of his foes.

5. Open-handed, he gives to the poor;|
   his justice stands firm for ever.
   His head will be raised in glory.
   The wicked man sees and is angry,|
   grinds his teeth and fades away;
   the desire of the wicked leads to doom.

6. Glory be to the Father, and to the Son
   and to the Holy Spirit,
   as it was in the beginning, is now and ever shall be
   world without end. Amen.

4. SCRIPTURE READING

5. RESPONSORY

This has the function of a response or comment on the Reading.
A. Texts of the short responsories of Sunday evening prayer in ordinary time:

Weeks 1 & 3

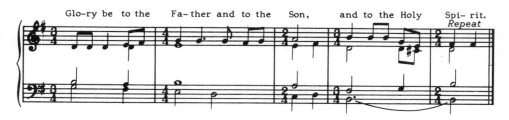

Res. **Great is our Lord:** **great is his might.** *Repeat*

V. His wis-dom can ne-ver be mea-sured. *Repeat Res.*

V. Glo - ry be to the Fa-ther and to the Son, and to the Ho-ly Spi-rit.
Repeat Resp.

Text © Bishop's Conference of England and Wales
Music © Stephen Dean

B. *Other pieces suitable to be used as responsories:*

Adoramus te Domine	696
Let it breathe on me	533
Dona nobis pacem	701
Glory be to the Father	702
Misericordias Domini	709
Sing and rejoice	713

any other meditative piece may be chosen.

6. GOSPEL CANTICLE

At Morning Prayer:	The Benedictus	693
At Evening Prayer:	The Magnificat	414,479,694
At Night Prayer:	The Nunc Dimittis	561, 695

7. INTERCESSIONS
   OUR FATHER
   CONCLUDING PRAYER

8. BLESSING

Divine Office part © Music Stephen Dean

Divine Office part © Music Mayhew-McCrimmon Ltd

Other Psalms in Volume 1 & 2 (including paraphrases and hymns):
Grail Psalms are in bold type.

CANTICLES AND HYMNS BASED ON SCRIPTURE

Old Testament:

New Testament:

722　THAXTED (13.13.13.13.13.13)

1. I vow to thee, my country, all earthly things above,
   entire and whole and perfect, the service of my love:
   the love that asks no questions, the love that stands the test,
   that lays upon the altar the dearest and the best;
   the love that never falters, the love that pays the price,
   the love that makes undaunted the final sacrifice.

2. And there's another country, I've heard of long ago,
   most dear to them that love her, most great to them that know;
   we may not count her armies, we may not see her King;
   her fortress is a faithful heart, her pride is suffering;
   and soul by soul and silently her shining bounds increase,
   and her ways are ways of gentleness and all her paths are peace.

Words: Sir Cecil Spring-Rice
Music: G. Holst 1874–1934

Music © J. Curwen & Son Ltd

Acknowledgements

The publishers would like to express their gratitude to the following for the use of their copyright material in this book:

Agape, Carol Stream, IL 60188, USA for Break not the circle © 1975; Divided our pathways © 1974; Help us accept each other © 1975; High light now shines in the darkness © 1969; Let us talents and tongues employ © 1975; Lord, confronted with your might © 1975; You, Israel, return now © 1976. International copyright secured. All rights reserved. Used with permission.
John Ainslie, 76 Great Bushey Drive, Totteridge, London N20 8QL for the tune "Ellenborough" (Grant us thy peace). Used by permission.
The American Catholic Press, 1223 Rossell Oak Park, Illinois 60302, USA for the words and music of O what a gift © 1967, 1970. Used by permission. All rights reserved.
Ampleforth Abbey Trustees, Ampleforth Abbey, York YO6 4EN for the words of O raise your eyes on high and see. Used by permission.
The Archdiocese of Durban, 408 Innes Road, Durban 4001, South Africa for the words of Across the years; God at creation's dawn; God, our maker; If God is our defender; Lord, this paschaltime; O light forever dawning; Send forth your Spirit; and for the words and music of Firm is our faith. All used with permission.
William Armitage, Canada, for the words of To God our Father © 1977.
Augsburg Publishing House, 426 South Fifth Street, Box 1209, Minneapolis, MN 55440, USA for This is the feast, reprinted from Contemporary Worship 2: The Holy Communion, © 1970; Christ has arisen, Alleluia! reprinted by permission from Lead us, Lord ed. by Howard S. Olson © 1977. Used by permission
Tony Barr, 9 Patmore Road, Colchester, Essex for the words and music of Rain down justice. Tony Barr and Jabulani Music, 9 Patmore Road, Colchester, Essex for My God you fathom my heart; The song of God among us (Lest he be too far from us); I lift up my eyes; Our help is the name of the Lord; Who wants to live as God (The song of all seed); Breath of life and Stand and Stare not. Music © Bernard Huijbers; Text © Huub Oosterhuis; Translation © Tony Barr. Used with permission.
The Benedictine Foundation of the State of Vermont, Weston Priory, Weston, Vermont 05161, USA for A child is born for us today © 1971; I lift up my eyes to the mountains © 1975; In the beginning © 1974, 1975; We thank you, Father © 1971, 1980. All used with permission.
The Benedictines of Stanbrook, Stanbrook Abbey Press, Callow End, Worcester WR2 4TD for the words and music of When Jesus comes to be baptized. Used with permission.
Laurence Bevenot OSB, St Mary's, 67 Talbot Street, Canton, Cardiff CF1 9BX for Christus Vincit. Used with permission.
Bmg. Music, Holland for the music of God's Spirit precedes us.
Mrs William Booth-Clibbon for the words and music of Let it breathe on me.
Breitkopf & Hartel, Buch und Musicverlag, Walkmuhlstrasse 52, Wiesbaden 1, West Germany for the music of Be still my soul. Used with permission.
Burckhardthaus Verlag GmbH, 6460 Gelnhausen 1, Germany, for the original words and music of Give us the will to listen. Used with permission.
Burnes & Oates, Wellwood, North Farm Road, Tunbridge Wells, Kent TN2 3DR for the music of Take my life and let it be; Who is she that stands triumphant. Used with permission.
Celebration Services (International) Limited, Cathedral of the Isles, Millport, Isle of Cumbrae, KA28 OHE, Scotland, for the words and music of Sons of God arise! © 1971, 1975; Be like your Father © 1979; Fear not, rejoice and be glad © 1971, 1975; Fear not, for I have redeemed you © 1975; I will sing, I will sing © 1974, 1975; Look around you (Kyrie Eleison); O be joyful in the Lord! © 1975; The eyes of the blind (God make us your family) © 1973, 1975; We cry "Hosanna, Lord" © 1975. All used with permission.
Chevalier Press, PO Box 13, Kensington, NSW 2033, Australia for the words and music of Father in my life (Trinity Song). Reproduced from "Eagles Wings" by Fr Frank Anderson, MSC. Used with permission.
Christian Conference of Asia, 480 Lorong 2, Toa Payoh, Singapore 1231, on behalf of D.P. Niles and E.G. Maquiso for Father in heaven © 1961. Used with permission.
Collins Liturgical Publications, 187 Piccadilly, London W1V 9DA for the following Taize material: Adoramus Te, Jubilate Deo, Jubilate Servite, Misericordias Domini and Ostende Nobis. Copyright © 1978, 1980, 1981 Les Presses de Taize (France). International Copyright Secured. All Rights Reserved. Used with permission.
Anne Conway, St Joseph's School, Upper Lindum Street, Lincoln LN2 5RW for the words and music of As earth that is dry (Come to the waters); Lord graciously hear us; Sing everyone a song to the Lord; This is the day. Used with permission.
J. Curwen & Sons Ltd., Stockley Close, Stockley Road, West Drayton, Middlesex UB7 9BE for the words and music of Hills of the north rejoice, from Curwen Edition number 80634, and for the music of I vow to thee my country. Used with permission.
Stewart Cross, Ribchester Road, Blackburn BB1 9EF for the words of Father, Lord of all creation. Used with permission.
Margaret Daly, Eire, for the words of When the time came © 1978. Used with permission.

Bill Tamblyn, 28 Priory Street, Colchester, Essex, for the music of Bartimaeus © 1980; To God our Father be the praise © 1980; Wind and fire © 1980; Go out to the whole world © 1975; I rejoiced © 1975. Used with permission.

Tembo Music Limited, 50 Regent's Park Road, Primrose Hill, London NW1 7SX for the music of I saw a star. Used with permission.

Thankyou Music, PO Box 75, Eastbourne BN23 6NW for the words and music of Bind us together by Bob Gillman © 1977; Our God reigns by L.E. Smith Jnr. © 1974/78; Father, I place into your hands by J.Hewer © 1975. Used with permission.

Eric A. Thorn, 17 Rowan Walk, Crawley Down, West Sussex for the words of I met you at the cross.

Honor Mary Thwaites for the words of A mighty stronghold. Used with permission.

Mrs J.Tyrrell, 41 Minster Road, Godalming, Surrey GU7 1SR for the words of Lord of all power. Used with permission.

United Reformed Church, 86 Tavistock Place, London WC1H 9RT for the words of Almighty Father and for the music of Lord of all power. Used with permission.

Tom Van Erp, Wychen, Nederlands for the music of Son of God and son of David.

Verlag Merseburger Berlin, GmbH, Buro Kassel, 35 Kassel, Motzstrasse 13. West Germany for the words and music of Sing and rejoice in the Lord.

Chrysogonus Waddell & St Joseph's Abbey, Mount St Joseph's Abbey, Roscreen, Co Tipperary, Eire for the words and music of O Comfort my people.

Christopher Walker, Master of Music, Clifton Cathedral, Bristol for the music of Alleluia (Premananda); Alleluia (Ps.116); Give thanks to the Lord (Ps.117); Veni Sancte Spiritus, and for the translation of Veni Sancte Spiritus. Used with permission.

Joseph Walshe OSCO, Mount Melleray Abbey, Cappoquin, Co Waterford, Eire for By his wounds (Christ suffered for you). Words and music. Used with permission.

Jose Webber for the music of Greater love © 1970.

Josef Weinberger Limited, 12–14 Mortimer Street, London W1N 8EL for the words and music of Lord, in everything I do   1979. Used with permission.

The Word of God Music, PO Box 8617, Ann Arbor, MI 48107, USA for the words and music of Alleluia! Give thanks © 1973; I heard the Lord call my name © 1973; The light of Christ © 1974. Used with permission.

World Council of Churches, Geneva, for the use of the following harmonization from "Cantate Domino" (1980 edition): Let all who share one bread; Modern Man. Used with permission.

World Library Publications Inc., 5040 Ravenswood, Chicago, Illinois 60640, USA for the words and music of All the earth © 1965; All you nations © 1965; Keep in mind © 1965; My soul is longing © 1965; Send forth your spirit © 1965; The spirit of God © 1970; There is one Lord © 1965; Alleluia (Ps.150) © 1964; Pasch of the new law © 1965, 1966, 1973; Give praise to the Lord, and for the words of Shepherd of Souls © . Reprinted with permission.

World Student Christian Federation, Geneva, for the words of Thine be the glory. Used with permission.

John C. Ylvisaker, Minneapolis, Minnesota 55423, USA for the words and music of It's good to give thanks to the Lord; Now let your people depart in peace © 1979; We are bound for the promised land © 1979. Used with permission.

All or part of the copyright of the following is vested in Mayhew McCrimmon Limited, 10–12 High Street, Great Wakering, Essex SS3 0EQ:

Hymn Nos. 388, 392, 393, 394, 403, 406a, 408, 414, 415, 418, 420, 422, 423, 425, 434, 436, 437, 438, 458, 464, 465, 466, 467, 471, 481, 484, 485, 491, 493, 494, 502, 503, 507, 509, 512, 513, 517, 520, 522, 529, 530, 533, 536, 538, 539, 541, 553, 555, 556, 559, 560, 561, 562, 563, 566, 572, 576, 579, 580, 581, 584, 586, 588, 589, 591, 595, 598, 600, 601, 602, 603, 612, 615, 620, 624, 626, 632, 634, 637, 640, 641, 643, 644, 650, 651, 654, 661.

Psalms: 667(22), 668(23), 669(24), 674(62), 676(84), 683(114), 691(144).   The Benedictus 693.

Rounds: 705, 708, 712, 716, 717, 718, 719, 720, 721.

The Divine Office is © to The Grail, the Bishop's Conference of England and Wales, Stephen Dean and Mayhew McCrimmon Limited.

Complete Index of tunes

INDEX OF TUNES

Complete Metrical index

Sometimes a hymn has words which are suitable for a particular occasion but its tune is unfamiliar. Using this section, another tune can be chosen to fit the words.

To use it, look at the numbers after the hymn title (for example, ROCKINGHAM (88 88), No.202). Then look at the 88.88 section here to find other tunes in the same metre. The first line has been given here as well as the name, to help you recognise the tunes. (You can also consult the Metrical Index of another hymn book for extra choise.)

A word of caution: try out the words and tune together before choosing. Sometimes the syllables of the lines may be equal in number but the accents of the words are different.

Not all the tunes are listed here. Some of the modern songs have special metres and are always sung to the same tune. Christmas carols and hymns with irregular metres are not listed either.

66.66

S6	Hail, holy Joseph (Lisbon)
151	Jesu, meek and lowly (Ravenshaw)
290	Star of ocean, lead us (Ave maris stella)
549	Lord, thy word abideth = 151

66.86 (Short Metre, SM)

36	Blest are the pure in heart (Franconia)
37	Breathe on me, breath of God (Carlisle)
180	Lord Jesus, think on me (Southwell)
301	The coming of our God (Optatus)
333	To Christ, the prince of peace (Narenza)

77.77

80	Forty days and forty nights (Heinlein)
= 608	Take my life
82	From the depths I cry to thee (Culbach)
120	Holy Father, God of might (Vienna)
171	Let us, with a gladsome mind (Monkland)
187	Loving shepherd of thy sheep (Lubeck)
339	Virgin wholly marvellous (Orientis Partibus)
(608	– see 80)

86.86 (Common Metre, CM)

S5	St Andrew, called to follow Christ
15	All ye who seek a comfort sure (St Bernard)
18	Almighty Father, take this bread (Farrant)
19	Amazing grace (Amazing grace)
50	Come, Holy Ghost, creator, come (Tallis' Ordinal)
115	Help, Lord, the souls (Belmont)
= 201	My God, accept my heart this day
136	In Christ there is no east nor west (McKee)
152	Jesu, the very thought of thee (Jazer)
183	Lord, who throughout these forty days (St Flavian)
= 198	Most ancient of all mysteries
(201	– see 115)
203	My God, how wonderful thou art (Westminster)
204	My God, I love thee (Everlasting Love)
217	O Father, now the hour has come (Unity)
218	O Father, take in sign of love (Horsley)
= 316	There is a green hill far away
222	O God, our help in ages past (St Anne)
224	O God, we give ourselves today (Irish)

262	Praise to the holiest (Billing
308	The head that once was crowned with thorns (St Magnus)
= 570	O raise your eyes on high
312	The Lord's my shepherd, I'll not want (Crimond)
315	The race that long in darkness pined (i: St Fulbert = 363 (ii: Dundee)
(316	– see 218)
360	While shepherds watched (Winchester Old)
363	Ye choirs of new Jerusalem (St Fulbert = 315)
408	Before Christ died (Lindisfarne)
432	City of God (Richmond)
454	Father of heaven, whose love profound (Song 5)
(570	– see 308)
613	The King shall come (Consolation)
631	Through all the changing scenes (Wiltshire)

87.87

34	Bethlehem! of noblest cities (Stuttgart = 439ii)
42	Christ is King of earth and heaven (Laus Deo or Redhead No.46)
= 275	See us, Lord, about thine altar
75	Firmly I believe and truly (Omni die)
112	Hark! a herald voice is calling (Merton)
130	I believe in God the Father (Sussex)
= 449	Father, hear the prayer we offer
184	Love divine, all loves excelling (Love divine)
(275	– see 42)
311	The King of love my shepherd is (Dominus regit me)
385	Across the years (St Columba (Erin))
388	All for Jesus
439	Come, thou long-expected Jesus (i : Cross of Jesus ii: Stuttgart)
(449	– see 130)

88.88 (Long Metre, LM)

2	Accept, O Father, in thy love (Breslau)
10	All people that on earth do dwell (Old 100th)
17	Almighty Father, God most high (Tallis' Canon)
= 91	Glory to thee, my God, this night
61	Dear maker of the starry skies (Creator alme siderum)
73	Fight the good fight (Duke Street)

METRICAL INDEX

METRICAL INDEX

(462 – see 166)
543   Lord, enthroned in heavenly splendour

88.88.88

67   Eternal Father, strong to save (Melita)
71   Father, within thy house today (Surrey)
213   O bread of heaven (St Catherine)
295   Sweet Saviour, bless us ere we go (Sunset)

65.65D

109   Hail, thou star of ocean (Laudes)
188   Maiden, yet a mother (Une vraie crainte)

66.86D (Double Short Metre, DSM)

56   Crown him with many crowns (i: Corona
                       ii: Diademata
90   Glory to thee, Lord God = 56(i)

76.76D

8   All glory, laud and honour (St Theodulph)
13   All things bright and beautiful (Royal Oak)
110   Hail to the Lord's anointed (Cruger)
132   I'll sing a hymn to Mary (Turris Davidica)
142   I sing the Lord God's praises (Magnificat)
149   Jerusalem the golden (Ewing)
176   Look down, O mother Mary (Vaughan)
221   O God of earth and altar (i: Kings Lynn
                       ii: Willsbridge)
233   O Jesus Christ, remember (Aurelia)
= 300   The Church's one foundation
= 516   If God is our defender
234   O King of might and splendour
                    (O King of might)
247   O sacred head, sore-wounded
                    (Passion Chorale)
= 569   O light forever dawning
= 577(i)   Our Father, we have wandered
(300 – see 233)
302   The day of resurrection (Ellacombe)
332   Thy hand, O God, has guided (Thornbury)
429   Christ is the world's redeemer (Moville)
433   Come, God's people, sing for joy
                    (Ave virgo virginum)
497   Help us accept each other (Baronita)
(516 – see 233)
(569 – see 247)
(577(i) – see 247)
577 (ii)   Our Father, we have wandered (Neshanic)

77.77D

27   At the Lamb's high feast we sing (Salzburg)
40   By the blood that flowed from thee
                    (Westminster Old)
55   Come ye thankful people, come (St George)
107   Hail redeemer, King divine (King divine)
150   Jesus, lover of my soul (Aberystwyth)
286   Songs of thankfulness and praise
                    (St Edmund)
545   Lord, in everything I do (Charlton)

86.86D

25   Attend and keep this happy fast (Claudius)
156   Jesus is God! the solid earth
                    (Ellacombe, modified)
208   Now come to me, all ye who seek (Come to me)
235   O little town of Bethlehem (Forest Green)
344   We celebrate this festive day

87.87D

7   Alleluia! sing to Jesus (Hyfrydol)
57   Daily, daily, sing to Mary (i: Daily daily
                      ii: Laudes Mariae
98   God of mercy and compassion (Au sang qu'n Dieu)
103   Great St Andrew, friend of Jesus (Contemplation)
163   Leader now on earth no longer (Swavesey)
281   Sing of Mary, pure and lowly (Pleading Saviour)
453   Father, Lord of all creation (Abbot's Leigh)
= 472   Glorious things of thee are spoken
483   God our maker, mighty Father (Rex Gloriae)
585   Praise the Lord! ye heavens, adore him (Austria)

Complete Index of uses

1b. SACRAMENTS AND RITES

BAPTISM: see Christian Initiation

BENEDICTION: see Worship of the Eucharist

CHRISTIAN INITIATION:

N.B. The following categories overlap to some extent.

Catechumenate

see also God's love and care; Our love of God; Praise; Thanksgiving; Trust

Celebration of Baptism

see also the preceding category; and Confirmation, Church, Communion (Mass Section)

Baptism at the Easter Vigil

THE BODY AND BLOOD OF CHRIST (CORPUS CHRISTI)
(see:Communion, Maundy Thursday)

Complete Index of first lines

INDEX OF FIRST LINES

INDEX OF FIRST LINES

INDEX OF FIRST LINES

INDEX OF FIRST LINES